Spires of Form

SPIRES
OF FORM

Glimpses
of Evolution

VICTOR B. SCHEFFER

*University of
Washington Press*

SEATTLE & LONDON

Drawings by Gretchen Daiber

Library of Congress Cataloging in Publication Data

Scheffer, Victor B.
  Spires of form.

  Bibliography: p. 139
  Includes index.
  1. Evolution. I. Title.
QH366.2.S3 1983   591.3'8   83-47972
ISBN 0-295-96037-X

A subtle chain of countless rings
The next into the farthest brings,
And, striving to be man, the worm
Mounts through all the spires of form.

RALPH WALDO EMERSON
May-Day (1867)

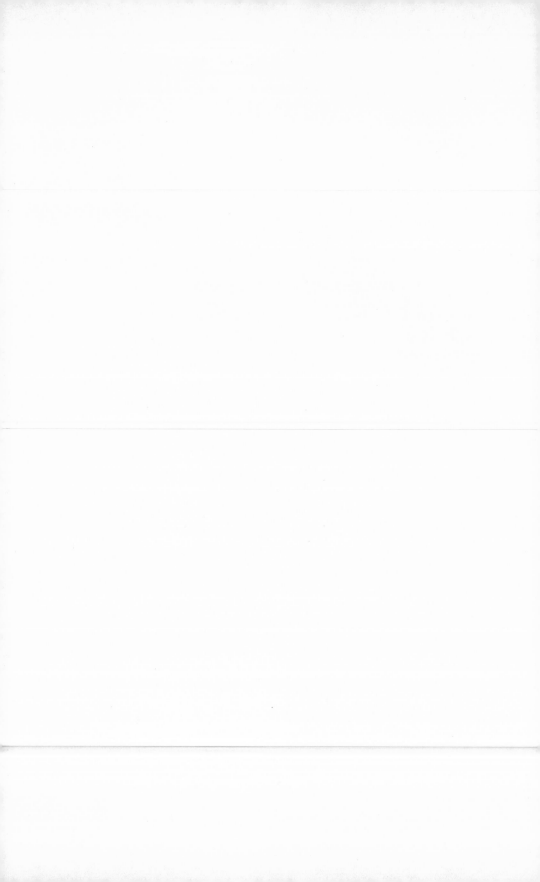

Contents

How They Breed   72

Seaworms, Tumblebugs, and Starfishes.
A Lifelong Attachment.
The Fish That Must Die for Its Young.
Frogs That Give Birth Through the Mouth.
The Worst Journey in the World.
The Loneliest of Birds. Virgin Birth. Sex Ambivalence.
The Meaning of Sex Ratios.
McClure and Her Wood Rats. Hermaphroditism.
The Salamander That Breeds in Youth.

Life in Populations   94

The Rewards of Hostility. Calhoun and His White Mice.
The Meaning of Clutch-Size. Cyclic Populations.
Group Selection.

Tempo and Mode in Evolution   107

The Rate of Speciation. No Two Alike.
The Direction of Evolution. Evolutionary Success.
Where is Human Evolution Headed?

Illustration Credits   127

Reference Notes   129

For Further Reading   139

Index   145

Spires of Form

Charles Darwin

Introduction

In THE WET GREEN FORESTS of coastal Oregon there live acrobatic mice. Properly called tree mice, they live the year around in tall fir trees, giving birth in nests that they build from slender twigs and fibers. They depend for food on fresh needles and sprigs of fir.

Compared to their nearest earthbound relatives—the heather mice—tree mice give birth to fewer offspring and need more time to raise them. Tree mice don't scurry along their swaying pathways in the sky but travel slowly and carefully. Their long tails serve as balancing poles. One of my friends who keeps tree mice in a pen for study has found that they can be picked up easily; they rarely bite if not held too tightly.

The peculiarities of tree mice call for understanding. Perhaps the mice produce few young because they don't *need* to, for their survival rate is higher than that of mice that live on the ground and are daily exposed to attack by predatory weasels, owls, and foxes. Perhaps tree mice can't *afford* to breed faster, living as they do on energy-poor food. And perhaps their offspring mature slowly because they need extra time to gain acrobatic skills.

If the tree mouse did not exist and I were told to design one, I could hardly improve on Nature's product—a small, sure-footed beast dressed in the protective colors of fir-tree cones, adapted to a resinous diet, and adapted to moving about in a narrow ecological niche.

This book is about animal evolution. It is designed for readers who have little or no formal training in biology. It is neither rigorous nor comprehensive, so if you are looking for textbooks on evolution, I refer you to the section "For Further Reading." It often employs real-

Oregon tree mouse

life examples, singling out those peculiarities of animal form, function, and behavior that illuminate the evolutionary process. Examples are drawn from the invertebrates, the fishes, the amphibians, the reptiles, the birds, and the mammals.

It tells of animal fitness for life, or the remarkable fit of all animals within their surroundings. When the surroundings change, as they must in time, Nature preserves the closeness of fit by eliminating those individuals least able to change. The process is natural selection, a process that is both Nature's way of shaping the animal species and the species' way of adapting. Natural selection is elimination of the unfit through trial and error. (I shall have more to say later about the meaning of "unfit.")

And the book is a personal tribute to animals—to their beauty and elegance of function, their complexity, and their staying power. An Old Testament writer marveled at "the way of an eagle in the air; the way of a serpent on a rock." And still in the age of science we wonder how the eagle and the serpent play so exactly their appointed roles in the drama of life. We marvel at their strategies for survival.

When we try to understand the lives of animals and try to *be* those animals we enter another dimension. We begin to feel as men and women will someday feel when first they talk with sensitive beings on another world.

I should not like to be misunderstood. When I write of animals adapting or employing strategies I am using biological shorthand, for no animal except man has the slightest notion of its role in life, or holds to ideals, or can anticipate. For every wild animal the momentary problems of living are met with momentary solutions. Emerson's worm which, "striving to be man, mounts through all the spires of form," is a species known only to poets.

I should like also to make crystal clear that adaptation in its evolutionary sense applies to species (populations) and not to individuals. We can conveniently assume that the capabilities of the individual are genetically fixed—are rigid. It is the species that adapts when certain individuals are weeded out while others, better able genetically to cope with hard times, survive to leave offspring that likewise will be able to cope.

So, every well-adapted species on earth has inherited those features of form and function that now enable it to exploit a particular niche and to solve the peculiar problems of that niche. I use the word niche (or econiche) as most biologists do, to mean not only the geographical habitat occupied by the species but, more importantly, the role that the species plays in the life of its community. Every species has both a space niche and a functional niche; these are properties of the species. Quite as two actors cannot play, simultaneously and on the same stage, the role of Hamlet, two different species occupying the same niche cannot long coexist. The one that has some inherent advantage over the other will, through competition, eventually drive it into local extinction. The tree mouse is said to occupy a narrow niche, not just because it lives only on the Pacific Northwest Coast but also because its diet is restricted almost entirely to evergreen needles and twigs. The common crow is said to occupy a broad niche because it is widely distributed over North America, takes advantage of many diverse habitats, and eats a wide variety of plant and animal foods.

Some biologists follow the convention of writing about animal behavior as (for example) *competition* among mice, *cannibalism* among fishes, *rape* among ducks, *divorce* among penguins, *warfare* among ants, and *altruism* among butterflies. Other biologists claim that these anthropomorphic terms are misleading, insofar as they imply parallels between human and nonhuman acts. Does it matter? Such emotive terms come rather easily to anyone who can, as Emerson could, see evolution as a grand organic poem.

Translating biological ideas for the benefit of readers who are not biologists is like translating poetry into a second language; shades of meaning are lost. This fact has not kept me from trying.

When I use the word Nature I do not mean a cosmic mother-figure but those unenacted laws—those natural processes—that determine how a beaver's egg shall become a beaver, how a beaver knows where to build its dam, how microbes recycle the body of a dead beaver, and how beavers came into being in the first place. When I write that a Mexican salamander has learned genetically to mate and to lay its eggs while still a tadpole I mean that Nature has tested various models of salamander and has allowed only this one to survive in the econiche it now fills.

I shall frequently mention the kind of behavior called instinctive, as opposed to that called reasoned. Instinct is the inborn tendency of an animal to respond to a certain stimulus in a certain way. It is genetically programmed. It explains the behavior of newly born (or newly hatched) animals when as yet they have learned nothing about their environment, and it explains the limitation of their capacity later in life to learn. In the great apes, at least, and perhaps in other nonhuman mammals, such as dolphins, whose mental processes are still being explored, instinct and learning are evidently supplemented by flashes of pure reason. Behavior is guided in the "lowest" organisms by native instinct alone, in the "higher" ones by instinct intertwined with learning, and in the "highest" ones by instinct, learning, and reason combined.

As one tries to understand the behavior of an animal it is not always easy to weigh the relative importance of native instinct and

later learning as determinants of that behavior. The ritual of a scarab beetle rolling a ball of dung in which to lay its egg, and that of a spider weaving the signature of its species, and that of a blind termite building its castle in the night, must be purely instinctive, for the juveniles of these animals can learn nothing from parents they will never see. On the other hand, experiments have shown that a male white-crowned sparrow raised in isolation in captivity where it can learn nothing from other sparrows will grow up singing an imperfect song.[1] Native instinct alone will not establish in the developing bird a full vocal repertoire. If, however, during the critical period from ten to fifty days after the sparrow hatches it is exposed to a tape recording of a typical sparrow song, it will learn that song and will, when mature, repeat it faithfully.

If a homing pigeon is raised in a light-tight room, prevented from seeing the sun in the morning, and allowed to practice flying only in the afternoon, it will never learn to use the sun for orientation and homing.[2] The afternoon arc of the sun is not enough to establish a sun compass for the entire day. Nonetheless, the bird will home accurately by use of its inborn magnetic compass (crystals of magnetite within its brain). Thus the pigeon's homing behavior is partly based on instinct and is partly learned.

"A kitten watches at a mouse-hole," mused Edward Blyth in 1836, "though it has never seen a mouse."[3]

When I write of "lower" and "higher" animals I do so with some embarrassment, for modern biologists do not widely agree that animals can, or should, be ranked in this fashion. Darwin, however, found it convenient to label as lower those species that *in general* are simpler, slower to change, and geologically older; and as higher those that are more complex, quicker to change, and geologically younger (later-evolved). I emphasize the disclaimer, *in general*, for a lineage that has experienced greater change from ancestral forms than a related lineage will not necessarily end as being more complex.

And I don't imply that an ape is any more remarkable or better than a worm, for the two creatures are equally astonishing in the pure fact of their existence. "Monkeys," says evolutionist George Gaylord Simpson, "are better at being monkeys than we would be even if we tried."[4]

The Counted
and the Uncounted

It seems that Nature has taken pleasure in varying
the same mechanism in an infinity of different ways.
She abandons one type [*genre*] of product only after
having multiplied individuals in all possible modes.

DENIS DIDEROT
Pensées sur l'interpretation de la nature (1754)

PLANET EARTH SUPPORTS a million known species of animals
and at least a million (mostly insects) yet undiscovered. They live on
the surface of the ground and beneath it; in rivers, lakes, and seas;
and upon or within plants and animals. Mountain climbers on Everest see spiders in the thin, sharp air at 22,000 feet elevation. Ocean-
ographers dredge living organisms from the black, awful waters
36,000 feet below the surface of the sea. Along the mid-ocean rifts
where molten rock spews from the earth's deep mantle and strikes
the sea it creates warm, sulfurous domains where tube worms eight
feet long, white crabs and fishes, "dandelion" hydroids, and other
fantastic animals live. In these domains, first explored in 1977, biologists are finding not only new species, but wholly new systems.[1]
The tube worms lack eyes, mouth, gut, and anus. They absorb
hydrogen sulfide, a gas extremely toxic to man, through their skin
and use it indirectly for synthesizing food. Symbiotic bacteria
swarming inside each worm oxidize the hydrogen sulfide and cap-
ture, for their own needs, energy released in the process; the worm
then digests the bacterial biomass. Perhaps it was some hellish place
like the margin of a mid-ocean rift that served as the cradle of life
itself. Rather recently a dwarf fauna was discovered among sand
grains and mud particles on the ocean floor. Termed *psammon* (from

Seashells on a Mexican shore

the Greek word for sand), this fauna contains species that live nowhere else and that were previously unknown.

The desert pupfishes of the Death Valley region of southern California and adjacent Nevada—souvenirs of the Ice Age—live as easily
in fresh-water pools as in pools having a salinity near that of sea water.[2] They adapt to temperatures ranging from a near-freezing 38 degrees Fahrenheit to a near-scalding 108 degrees, or even, for several
minutes, to 111 degrees. The smallest, the Devil's Hole pupfish, is
no longer than the last joint of a man's thumb.

If, some day, there is to be erected a Living Museum of Nature it
ought to include among its exhibits a few pupfishes, along with Darwin's finches, New Zealand tuataras, a duckbilled platypus or two,
and other peculiar species that have advanced our knowledge of animal evolution.

Nevada pupfish

The largest animal on earth may be a female blue whale roaming somewhere in the Southern Ocean, if she has escaped the whale killers. She would weigh about two hundred tons and measure one hundred feet from snout to tip of tail. The smallest animal is a mesozoan, a translucent, wormlike creature composed of no more than twenty or thirty cells. It lives parasitically in the kidney urine of octopuses and cuttlefishes—surely one of the strangest environments of any animal. Measuring shorter than one-hundredth of an inch, it could curl up in a circle the size of the period at the end of this sentence.

And the freest of animals is perhaps the common swift of Great Britain, a bird that spends a good part of its life in the air.[3] It takes all its food—insects and spiders—on the wing. It drinks and bathes in falling rain or in shallow pools without alighting. In flight at sixty miles an hour it can elude most of its enemy birds of prey. Unique among birds, it mates in the air, holding contact for a few seconds only. It collects nesting material from grass-blades, seed-fluff, cocoons, and feathers borne aloft on summer breezes. And at the end of summer it leaves Britain for a nonstop flight of several thousand miles to southern Africa.

The presence of life in every conceivable habitat can best be appreciated if one thinks of life as a restless, probing, special state of matter. Life is an animate capability, forming and dissolving unions, now pressing into some vacant passageway and now being stopped where it can go no farther.

And in the fact that prebiotic molecules had to cooperate as well as compete while they were organizing complex assemblies, moralists find the roots of morality.

The Oldest Animals

Life on Earth began about four billion years ago. A sterile planet became a living world. Nascent life trembled for a while in molecular clusters that fragmented and reformed until they had "learned" to grow and reproduce. Those subvital clusters fed at times as scavengers and at times as cannibals.

The first true organisms, microscopic in size, reproduced by constricting at the middle and dividing in two. Subsequently, each daughter grew to the critical size at which its energy profits exceeded its energy losses—the size at which it was earning from its environment more than it was spending merely to sustain life—when it, too, divided. You and I are descended in an unbroken line from First Life. We are part of a continuum stretching through time and space.

There's an alternative scenario for the origin of life. Some believe that life could not have originated on a planet as young and as tiny as Earth. They believe that it began far out in our galaxy and eventually reached Earth as a frozen passenger on cometary debris or as a genetic template driven Earthward by the solar winds. Since the universe is known to be an enormous reservoir of organic molecules—the building blocks of life—Earth could well have been seeded by panspermia (literally, "everywhere seeded"). Hoyle and Wickramsinghe, British astronomers, champion the theory of panspermia on the grounds that interstellar dust has optical qualities similar to those of "hollow biological corpses."[4]

According to a variation on the panspermia scenario, life reached Earth via rocket from another planet. If such directed panspermia did in fact take place, there must have existed, four billion years ago, extraterrestrial beings who had already attained levels of intelligence superior to ours in the twentieth century after Christ.

If you choose to believe in panspermia, perhaps you should choose its directed, as against its accidental, version. Germs of life riding swiftly in a space-missile's hold, perhaps a missile deliberately aimed at Earth, would be more likely to arrive on target in good health than germs drifting naked through the ionizing beams of the cosmos. But regardless of where life began, the story of its subsequent evolution on Planet Earth remains the same.

There's an amusing page in the history of science where the discovery of Urschleim ("primal ooze") is described. This supposed archetype of life was a gelatinous substance containing microscopic, tapioca-like granules, dredged in 1857 from deep-sea muds. Thomas Huxley gave it a scientific name—Bathybius.[5] Although he was an outstanding scientist, he was also a mystic, and he reverently carried his belief in primal ooze for twenty years—to the moment in 1878 when he learned that identical oozes could be produced simply by dumping plankton specimens into astringent preservative fluids. Farewell Bathybius!

The oldest rocks of Earth showing evidence of life preserve the fossils of one-celled, microbial species only. Newer rocks contain fossils increasingly complex and strange, such as those of the great flying reptiles and the dragonflies with a wingspan of more than two feet. The very newest rocks contain the fossils of animals closely resembling the species that surround us today.

Fossil traces of the first true animals are known from rocks about 700 million years old, a little older than the rocks on the floor of the Grand Canyon. ("True" animals were the first organisms dependent upon other forms of life for nutrition.) These animal traces are ghostly imprints left in oceanic muds that later turned to stone. They resemble no modern animals. They have been called paleocreatures in search of relatives.[6] Some are remindful of the "angels" that children make by falling in new snow and waving their arms.

Rather quickly, as geological time is measured, increasing numbers of animals began to prey on their fellows, with the result that smaller organisms found advantage in having defensive shells. Shells proved useful also as architectural members, providing support for food-gathering organs and body protection for tunneling species. With the emergence of hard-shelled forms in late Precambrian time, the true fossil record could begin. Untold numbers of species have appeared and disappeared since the deep Grand Canyon rocks were formed, most of them destined to remain as forever unknown to humankind as the movements of a Neanderthal dance.

Ants and redwoods, crabs, violinists, and toadstools are related by common origin. The evidence is compelling:
• All living things are composed of cells, and the fine structure of all cells as seen through the electron microscope is remarkably similar. Its primary message is LIFE.
• The chemistry of living and growing is likewise similar for all organisms. While the metabolism—the tapping of energy and using it to build and degrade molecules—varies from one species to the next, its basic chemistry is universal.
• And, at the point of reproducing, every organism follows a directive hidden in one of the two closely related families of nucleic acids, DNA (deoxyribonucleic acid) or RNA (ribonucleic acid). Although DNA and RNA are infinitely variable in detail, their double-helix configuration appears to be uniform throughout the living world.

How Many Kingdoms?

Neanderthal men and women would doubtless have had a name for every kind of plant and animal important in their daily lives. Even now, aboriginal folk taxonomies of average size distinguish about five hundred categories (such as oak, pine, and catfish) corresponding roughly to scientific genera.[7] In 1735 the Swedish naturalist Carolus Linnaeus published *Systema Naturae*, the first scholarly list of what he called the world's "animals, vegetables, and minerals."[8] He listed 4,235 species of animals, or fewer than one-half of one percent of those that biologists list today. We continue to acknowledge his priority in the field of systematic biology by attaching the letter L to each name, such as *Homo sapiens* L., that he coined.

In the following centuries, man's understanding of organic evolution grew explosively. Biologists discovered that the real differences among organisms lie at microscopic and chemical levels of organization and that thousands of species are neither plant nor animal in the classical sense. With the aid of the electron microscope, photospectrometer, gas chromatograph, and synchrotron radiation probe, biologists began to "see" living things as Linnaeus could not have dreamed of seeing them.

So, a five-kingdom arrangement of life is now widely accepted.[9] The kingdoms are:

MONERA. The bacteria, including forms once called the blue-green algae. Their genetic material is diffuse, not enclosed in a nucleus. Because many can be identified only by their chemistry, and because they mutate rapidly, giving rise to new kinds, bacteria are often classified as strains, isolates, types, breeds, clones, or stocks, as well as species.

PROTISTA. Algae and other water-inhabiting or damp-adapted species such as dinoflagellates, slime molds, and amoebas. All have a nucleus. While most are small and one-celled, some are macroscopic and are organized in spongy or tissue-like masses. This kingdom has been likened to a ragbag holding miscellaneous organisms which reflect "profound evolutionary experimentation."[10]

PLANTAE. The typical plants. Composed of organized tissues, nearly all are autotrophic (self-feeding; capable of synthesizing certain compounds—especially carbohydrates—necessary for life). Nearly all are inactive, insensible, and green.

FUNGI. The molds, mushrooms, and relatives. All are heterotrophic (other-feeding; dependent on other organisms, living or dead, for certain vital compounds). None is green.

ANIMALIA. The typical animals. All are heterotrophic, typically active, and sentient. In size and shape they are less variable than are plants. (Compare, if you will, a mouse and an ivy plant.)

The beauty of the five-kingdom scheme is that it offers a flashback to the early course of evolution. No one has yet shown, nor is likely to show, that primitive bacteria differed substantially from bacteria now living and presumed their lineal descendants. Moreover, the five-kingdom scheme emphasizes that what really distinguishes the members of one kingdom from those of another is not their material forms but their capabilities.

Left out of the five-kingdom scheme are the viruses. These are acellular and are widely held to be nonliving. Although a virus is self-replicating, it cannot reproduce itself outside a living host cell. According to one theory, viruses are stripped-down bacteria; according to another, genes or other protoplasmic particles that long ago escaped the control of whatever life systems brought them into being. Some of the very smallest ones, the viroids, are less than one-tenth the size of ordinary viruses and are evidently no more than short lengths of RNA. Perhaps we should regard the viruses as neither living nor nonliving but simply as molecular aggregates, the position of which on the *scala naturae* has yet to be determined.

Before the end of the twentieth century we may need a new taxonomy, one that will accept the singular organisms being created by genetic engineers as they put novel genes into the cells of old, familiar species. The engineers are as tickled by the marvels of new life at the molecular level as must have been the neo-Galilean astronomers by all the new lights suddenly filling their sky.

How did the five kingdoms arrive at their present diversity? Perhaps by *serial endosymbiosis*, or progressive cooperation among primitive microbes.[11] Proponents of this theory maintain that ancient amoebas engulfed aerobic bacteria and held them in slavery as organelles (organs of the cell). Countless generations later, the descendants of these amoebas captured whiplike bacteria, held them by one end, and used them as flagella (propellers or "swimfins"). Still later, certain flagellated amoebas captured photosynthetic (blue-green) bacteria and became the first plants, while others did not and became the first fungi and animals. In short, perhaps every cell in every modern plant, fungus, or animal carries a legacy from moneran and protistan ancestors which had learned cooperation in the warm seas of the Archaean Period, three billion years ago.

Many modern animals, of course, exist symbiotically with smaller organisms such as bacteria, green algae, and protozoans. One of the more astonishing symbiotic pairs is exemplified by the deep-sea tube worm (already mentioned) and its internal bacteria. The distinction between modern symbionts and those ancient ones that may have served as intermediaries in the evolution of plants, fungi, and animals is that the modern partners are genetically separate selves, while the intermediaries would have contained a single genome (gene package). In modern symbiotic pairs, the smaller, in-house partner commonly takes carbon in the form of carbon dioxide from the environment and changes it into complex organic carbon compounds that the host partner can use. The host repays its partner in the coin of protein.

Diversity

The inventiveness of Nature during eons of time has brought diversity to the animal world. Diversity is the variety, or richness, or complexity of ecosystems. The simplest measure of diversity is the number of species per unit area. Compare, if you will, the number of land birds that breed in two regions of North America. While twenty-six species inhabit the Arctic Slope of Alaska, more than six hundred inhabit the jungles of Panama. Thus the diversity of breeding birds is twenty-three times greater in Panama than in northern Alaska.[12]

Diversity increased through biological time as one genetic strain after another pushed against its physical limitations of life—against extremes of temperature and moisture, pressure and wind, chemical concentrations, and solar radiation. As each kind of organism adapted to life within its econiche—within a range of physical-chemical conditions—its *tolerance* for those conditions became a part of its character as distinct as its body shape and color.

If there is one common task in which all Earth-caring men and women are steadily engaged, it is that of preserving biological diversity. Let me offer five reasons why diversity must be saved. (I'm grateful to The Nature Conservancy, a public-service organization, for suggesting some of the reasons).[13]

• Because it preserves stability. A diversified ecosystem has overlapping checks and balances which guarantee that the system as a whole is buffered against the impact of any particular change.

• Because it promises future benefits. The living world is a sort of Patent Office in which billions of working models are stored. Among these, surely, are many that will eventually prove useful in medicine, agriculture, industry, and the arts.

• Because it delights. A varied landscape is more pleasing than a monotonous one (unless you're a farmer producing food for the rest of us). Perhaps, indeed, our pleasure in diversity stems from primal roots, from early man's total awareness of his natural surroundings—from his animal alertness.

• Because it intrigues. Why, for example, should there be greater diversity of marine fishes and invertebrates in tropical waters than in polar waters? Perhaps because the tropics are more extensive and more stable than the polar regions, hence may have allowed species more space and time in which to specialize. Who can say? Anyway, the problem intrigues.

• And because we *should*. Preserving diversity for future men and women is a moral necessity. Above the entrance to one of the great Alexandrine libraries there were carved two thousand years ago the words, A SANITORIUM FOR THE MIND.[14] When Alexandria was plundered, an estimated half-million papyri and other documents were lost forever. The richness of Earth's living library of plants and animals is likewise irreplaceable. It is threatened less by violence than by ignorance and apathy. "As living creatures," said the State Department's James Buckley, "the more we understand of biological processes, the more wisely we will be able to manage ourselves. Thus, the needless extermination of a single species can be an act of recklessness. By permitting high rates of extinction to continue, we are limiting the potential growth of biological knowledge. In essence, the process is tantamount to book burning; but it is even worse in that it involves books yet to be deciphered and read."[15]

The more closely one examines the marvelous, interlocking specialties of animals, the more one is tempted to believe that some agency not yet demonstrated to mankind designed them. But one has only to study the mathematics of gene expression to concede that the ordinary agencies of mutation and recombination are capable of producing an almost infinite number of specialty designs. A gene system with 10,000 genes has 10^{3000} possible combinations, a figure enormously greater than the number of all known stars *times* the diameter of the known universe in miles.[16] Since each combination could be the blueprint for a species, the potential number of species is staggering.

Research in molecular genetics during the latter half of our century has greatly advanced our understanding of how mutations occur. It has shown that variation within species is far more common than Darwin supposed. Why, then, should we be surprised that every animal seems to display the best of all possible designs? "Biology," says Theodosius Dobzhansky, "cannot fathom whether life may be a part of some Cosmic Design. But biology does show that the evolution of life on earth is governed by causes that can be understood by human reason."[17]

A final word. Although Nature needs thousands or millions of years to create a species, man needs only a few dozen years to destroy one. Fifty-three species of birds are now represented by fewer than three hundred individuals per species, while sixty-four species of mammals are represented by fewer than a thousand.[18] The Eskimo curlew, the ivory-billed woodpecker, and the Caribbean monk seal vanished during my lifetime even as plans for saving them were being discussed.

The impressive *Global 2000* study released by the United States government in 1980 predicted that 15 to 20 percent of all living species could be gone by the year 2000, mainly through loss or pollution of their wild habitats.[19] Mass extinction on this scale would be unprecedented in human history.

"There seemed many great auks," wrote poet John Fowles, "till the last one was killed."[20]

Problems and Solutions

In the american tropics there lives a kind of fly that seems to know at all times *exactly* what it is up to. It is the human botfly, a pest roughly the size of a horsefly. Instead of laying its eggs directly on the skin of a human or a monkey, it ambushes a young mosquito, lays ten to fifty eggs on the body of the mosquito where they won't hinder its flight, and allows the mosquito to fly away.[1] If the mosquito then finds a human or a monkey victim, it alights and begins to suck blood. The radiant warmth of the victim's skin automatically ruptures the thin eggshells. A tiny maggot drops from each egg and bores its way into the skin. The maggot, after gorging under the skin for six to eight weeks, reaches full size, bores its way to the surface, drops to the ground, and pupates.

Perhaps an adult female botfly, upon seeing a monkey in the forest, would not even recognize it as a potential victim—as a repository for her eggs. This strange, roundabout relationship between a parasite and its host may have originated as follows. Primitive botflies laid their eggs on damp foliage, as some varieties of botfly still do. Dispersal of the eggs was left to the chance that a monkey would brush against the foliage. But a few of the primitive flies (call them lucky) proved to be mutants. They were genetically programmed to lay *their* eggs on the helpless bodies of young mosquitoes on the same foliage. Some of these mosquitoes eventually found warm-blooded victims, including monkeys. The eggs of the lucky botflies survived to reach more targets than did other eggs (laid on leaves) whose future depended on being brushed by a passing monkey. Gradually the lucky strain became the common strain.

Clearly, there is advantage to a botfly in entrusting its eggs to a messenger who will (as a mosquito does) deliver them quietly at night, when monkeys are asleep. A monkey awake and active during the day would be likely to swat a botfly bent on depositing eggs directly on its skin. It is unclear, though, why certain primitive botflies did not gradually become nocturnal and thus adept at laying their eggs on sleeping monkeys. The simplest conclusion is that the botfly habit of laying eggs on precisely the kind of insect equipped to deliver them originated in a chain of evolutionary accidents.

The life of the botfly and of every other animal is a continuous exercise in problem solving. The main problems are those of finding food, of coping with hard times, of defending oneself against rivals and enemies, and of reproducing. Life becomes a struggle for existence. But without struggle there could be no survival of the fittest and hence no Darwinian evolution.

The lives of even the simplest microbes can be seen as exercises in problem solving. Witness the magnetotactic bacteria, whose bodies are aligned with the earth's magnetic field. Northern hemisphere bacteria tend to swim north and southern hemisphere bacteria south. In Brazil, on the geomagnetic equator, north-seeking and south-seeking varieties are roughly equal in numbers. Why? Evidently because the earth's magnetic field lines, while pointing toward the poles, also point downward. The wandering microbe doesn't care where north and south are located; it does care which way is *down*, where the food-rich sediments lie.[2]

The aim of this chapter is broadly to sketch some of the adaptive features of anatomy, physiology, and behavior that enable animals to solve their problems. Employed collectively and simultaneously, these are often more effective than the strategies employed by that clever and calculating animal, man himself. Subsequent chapters will deal one by one with specific animal problems.

Adaptation Through Compromise

Nature's designing of an animal can be compared to man's designing of an automobile. When a Detroit engineer plans a new model he weighs the respective costs of providing speed, economy, beauty, and ease of repair. The product emerges as a compromise. So also does Nature design the animal, weighing (for example) the advantage of a

Alaskan fur seals

heavily armored body against that of a lighter and faster one. Every animal emerges as a multipurpose creation.

Take the Alaskan fur seal; in body size it is clearly a compromise. The average adult male weighs 430 pounds; the average female only 96 pounds. For the gain that size offers to the male when he's fighting for breeding territory, natural selection works continually to create a larger male body. But the larger he becomes, the greater the risk that he will crush his mate during copulation or will blindly trample his 10-to-12-pound pups. The present male-to-female weight ratio, 4.5 to 1, is thus the result of two adaptive forces working for untold millennia against each other.[3]

The adaptive value of many an animal structure is puzzling until one has studied it carefully and skeptically. What does a walrus use its tusks for? For defense against polar bears? For reproduction—that is, for fighting with rival males? For pulling its fat body out of the sea onto slippery ice? For digging shellfish foods? The last seems most probable, for the tusks show scratches of the kind they would get if pushed repeatedly along gravelly sea bottoms.

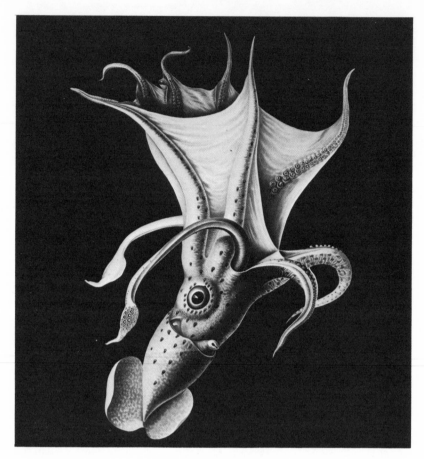

Luminescent squid

And what is the purpose of the rattlesnake's rattle? This buzzing appendage is widely supposed to be an advertisement warning larger animals neither to tread upon accidentally, nor to molest, its owner. The rattle has even been supposed to warn away other species for their own good, although Darwin cautioned in 1859 that "natural selection cannot possibly produce any modification in any one species exclusively for the good of another species."[4] The theory that seems most attractive is that the rattle draws a would-be predator's attention to the tail-end of the snake, thereby allowing the head-end time to strike.

And nipples on the breasts of men? Melvin Konner explains that the basic plan of the mammalian organism is female and stays that way unless told to be otherwise by masculine hormones."[5] These hormones are produced on genetic signal from the Y chromosome, which is present in males only. It might be said that, when the growing embryo is at the point of "deciding" whether to produce male or female sex characters, it can't make a clean decision . . . so newborn males emerge with nipples. The biological cost of nipples being slight, they have not been selected against.

Similarly, among mammals that have a penis bone, the females usually have a clitoris bone of variable shape and size. I have found this curious little structure in fur seals, land otters, and the archaic rodent called sewellel. Francis Fay found it in the walrus.[6]

The human coccyx, the terminus of the vertebral column that can be felt in the cleft between the buttocks, does not, like male nipples represent a mingling of sex characters but is witness to the fact that our remote ancestors had functional tails. The coccyx in children normally includes four distinct bones that fuse after puberty. Rarely, an infant is born with a flesh-and-bone tail up to two inches long.

The deep-sea luminescent squid is one of the most beautiful animals in the sea. Its body sparkles with light. When Carl Chun, oceanographer, was netting specimens in the Indian Ocean in the 1890s he hauled up a squid and placed it in a pan of sea water. Because it had known only cold, darkness, and enormous pressure it did not long survive at the surface. But as it lay dying it revealed the full glory of its light-producing organs. Chun wrote: "One would think that the body was adorned with a diadem of brilliant gems. The middle organs of the eyes shone with ultramarine blue, the lateral ones with a pearly sheen. Those towards the front of the lower surface of the body gave out a ruby-red light, while those behind were snow-white or pearly, except the median one, which was sky-blue."[7]

Biologists debate the purpose of the light-organs. Do they sparkle to confuse pursuing enemies? Do they attract and illuminate the small fishes upon which the squid feeds? Do they serve as sex lures during the mating season? Experiments that might furnish the answers are yet to be designed, for it is still unclear how one could spy upon a squid in its own realm without disturbing its normal behavior.

The squid swims, pointed-end first, by flapping its webbed arms much as one would open and close an umbrella. But does it swim a crooked course? Perhaps, for its left eye is twice the size of its right. This imbalance is indirect evidence that the squid migrates rhythmically up and down in the sea, using its big eye in deeper and darker waters and its small eye in shallower and brighter ones. Is there a better explanation?

Convergent Evolution

The squid's eye is rather like that of a human, a surprising fact when one considers that squids, being molluscs related to slugs, are far apart from humans on the Tree of Life. The molluscan eye, as well as the human eye, has a transparent cornea, an iris diaphragm, a focusing lens, and a retina. Our remote ancestors were hunters and gatherers, as presumably were ancestral squids. Faced with the common problem of quickly identifying food, the primitive molluscs and the prehominids hit upon similar designs for an eye. When two animals of unlike ancestry come gradually to resemble one another they are said to *converge*.

Cold-blooded fishes and warm-blooded dolphins have converged in shape and were once classified together because of their similarity. (Catholic law accepted the classification; it allowed the flesh of dolphins to be eaten on meatless Fridays.) Birds and bats, although having shared no common ancestor since Mesozoic time, developed wings when each took to the air. Most hole-nesting birds, such as woodpeckers and puffins, even if not closely related, lay white eggs. The more similar the econiches occupied by two animals, the more points of resemblance in body form and function will they tend to share. Nature, having hit upon certain practical blueprints for building an animal, uses them over and over again. Nature is parsimonious.

Partners and Antagonists

In the woods behind my surburban home there are down logs, and in the logs there are termites, and in the termites there are trichonymphs. Trichonymphs are microscopic protozoans that live only in the gut of termites. Each is equipped with flexible hairs that propel it erratically through the juices of the gut.

Many years ago a biologist observed that all termites contain trichonymphs and that these contain particles of wood previously swallowed by the termites. But wood is mainly cellulose (a polymer of glucose) and is for most animals indigestible. The biologist may have speculated, Are trichonymphs specialists in cellulose digestion? If so, the termite and its microbes are related as master and slaves. The master feeds on the sugar resulting from cellulose digestion, while the slaves get free board, room, and transportation.[8]

To test his idea he heated termites to increasingly higher temperatures until he arrived at one that killed the trichonymphs but not the termites. When, then, the termites cooled, they went back to chewing wood—but died of starvation. A theory had become a fact.

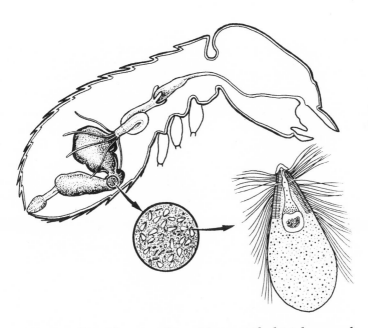

Section through a termite, with magnified trichonymph

Perhaps nowhere in the animal world is the struggle for existence more fierce than in marine tropical-reef communities. Here hundreds of fishes, shellfishes, and soft-bodied organisms interact daily. Here one can find the greatest variety of backboned animals living together. Here one can study competition, selective pressures, and specializations. A reef is a splendid place in which to learn what is meant by the phrase "adaptation for survival."

Rupert Ormond, a biologist who for years has been photographing reef communities in the Red Sea, writes about the trumpetfish, a small predator that "rides" a parrotfish or other large, slow-moving vegetarian species.[9] The trumpet swims closely aligned along and above the parrot's back. The trumpet hides within the general outline of the parrot until it sees an opportunity to attack. When the two happen to pass a prey organism, the trumpet "dismounts," dashes away, and grabs it. Some riding species like the chameleon wrasse actually change color, becoming darker or lighter to match their horses. And at least one wrasse changes pattern as well as color to imitate the striped goatfish that it rides!

Conrad Limbaugh, a diving instructor at Scripps Institution of Oceanography, lost his life in the sea in 1960. Though still a young man, he had become one of the world's foremost underwater naturalists. I was privileged to know him. It was his habit to take written notes of any unusual or mystifying behavior shown by a marine organism. The habit paid off, for he learned that a surprising number of sea creatures live by cleaning other marine organisms or themselves benefit by being cleaned. Connie Limbaugh is remembered for having unveiled the cleaning symbiosis.[10] Scores of undersea animals, including fishes, crabs, and shrimps, survive by cleaning. Some—the obligate cleaners—*must* clean for a living, while others—the facultative cleaners—clean only when they can't find more tasty food.

The charming little Pederson shrimp advertises itself as a cleaner by wearing a vivid pattern of white stripes and violet dots. It sets up shop in some quiet backwater where fish are accustomed to gather and, at the approach of a client, waves its long antennae and performs a ritual come-on dance. The willing client then halts and rests quietly while the shrimp grooms it of parasites and dead tissues. The cleaner devours these fleshy materials as its pay. A cleaner may even work inside the mouth of a larger fish which, in other circumstances, would devour the cleaner. (The lion allowing the lamb to lick its wounds.)

Connie explained that the client "usually presents its head or a gill cover for cleaning, but if it is bothered by something out of the ordinary, such as an injury near its tail, it presents itself tail first."[11] Rarely does a hungry client turn on its cleaner. "The immunity of certain cleaners is so well established that other fishes have come to mimic them in color and conformation and so share their immunity. Some mimics reverse the process and prey on the fish that mistake them for cleaners!"[12]

Parrotfish and bluehead wrasse

This convoluted procedure can be likened to a military game in which a Red Army soldier dons a white uniform in order to spy in White Army country. Not satisfied with moving about safely while he spies, he kills every White Army man who approaches him unafraid.

Connie, to be certain that he had rightly interpreted the cleaning symbiosis, carried out a field experiment. From two isolated reefs teeming with fish he removed all known cleaning organisms. Within two weeks most of the client fishes had disappeared, leaving only a few strongly territorial species. Many of these by now had developed fuzzy white blotches, swellings, open sores, and frayed fins.

In a final experiment he dropped a cleaner-shrimp into an aquarium containing diseased fishes. The shrimp began immediately to clean their infected tissues. Moreover, when Connie gently put his own hand into the aquarium, the little shrimp began reflexively to clean it, even picking at the fingernails.

Early in the history of life, Nature began to shape new species to fit into habitats already occupied by other species. Never since the Archaean Period has a living thing evolved alone. Whole communities have evolved as if they were one great organism. Thus all evolution is coevolution and the biosphere is now a confederation of dependencies.

So every animal is an obligate member of overlapping associations, and it behaves from birth as if it were mindful of its various memberships. It instinctively recognizes those fellow animals which will be its enemies and those upon which it will feed. It knows how to behave differently toward its near and its distant relatives. Animal associations can be grouped into four:

• Those beneficial to one associate. Witness the horse-and-rider relationship of reef fishes, wherein only the rider, a tolerated guest, is benefited. This association is commensalism, and the guest is a commensal.

• Those beneficial to both associates. Witness the termite-trichonymph relationship and the fish cleaner-client relationship. This association is symbiosis.

• Those harmful to one associate. Witness the botfly-monkey relationship (parasitism) and the luminiscent squid-foodfish relationship (predation).

• Those harmful to both associates. Warfare, or dominance competition within a species. ("Harmful," that is, to some of the individual combatants, but not to the species itself—*Homo sapiens* excepted.)

I once attended, as war correspondent, a skirmish between insect armies. On a warm day in June in my yard I watched about two hundred carpenter ants fighting. One ant would approach another face-to-face, thrust its antennae forward, and open wide its massive brown jaws. It would then seize the other in its jaws, at times with such vigor as to sever the slender neck or a leg of the opponent. It would either drag the victim away or move on to a fresh engagement. By late evening the warriors numbered only a dozen or so and the ground was littered with severed heads, limbs, and other bits. On the next day the battlefield was deserted.

This mini-war had broken out between two camps of ants competing for the same foraging ground. Each ant exuded an odorous chemical (a pheromone) that simultaneously identified its membership in one camp and antagonized ants from the other camp. Both camps smelled acidly alike to me.

The roots of warfare may lie in the kind of killing that goes on routinely within animal families and extended families. Young herons, eagles, owls, hawks, pelicans, skuas, and cranes often kill

Carpenter ants in battle

smaller siblings in the nest. A mother ground squirrel may kill the brood of another female and occupy the victim's nest. A starving elephant seal pup, having lost its mother, will try repeatedly to nurse from a strange female—at the risk of being severely bitten or killed. Under competitive stress, the killing of one animal by another of the same species is evidently more common than was once supposed.

It is not a far step from "murder" by individuals to warfare—a form of aggression practiced by social insects, by anthropoid apes, and by man.[13] Hominids in early Pleistocene time may have learned, first, to cooperate in small bands for hunting prey and for mutual defense against large predators. Later, they may have learned to join in larger bands to compete aggressively for desirable hunting territories or caves. Skirmishes among early men would have had survival value, for the strongest and brainiest fighters would have lived to perpetuate their kind.

But whether modern human warfare evolved genetically or culturally, or both, does not matter. It has become impersonal and mindless, destroying the best of the breeding stock along with the worst. "War," says Paul Shepard, "is the state's expression of social pathology."[14] By any civilized measure the costs of war far exceed its benefits.

To reflect upon the myriad strategies employed by animals for solving their problems is to think of an unbroken thread of life that originated forty million centuries ago. The spinning of that thread, were it not illuminated by the light of reason, would seem miraculous. But Willa Cather reminds us that miracles simply "rest . . . upon our perceptions being made finer, so that for a moment our eyes can see and our ears can hear what there is about us always."[15]

Their Daily Bread

Escorted by a prancing dog, I was hiking the other day along a tidal beach of Puget Sound. When I wasn't looking, the dog rubbed his back on a rotten starfish. I did not scold him for I knew that he had been provoked by a wolfish instinct beyond his control. An ancestral voice had told him to inform the leader of the hunting pack—which was me—that he had found food. To prove it he returned with a sample of the food in his fur.

Of all the problems that animals must solve, that of finding food is foremost. Every animal's life is an exercise in conservation. It is an exercise in cost accounting, where energy is the medium of exchange. Energy reaches the animal's body in sunlight and in food. If the animal breaks even, it survives; if it earns a profit, it reproduces.

Animals have a sense of spareness; they know exactly how little to do. The honeybee and the hummingbird know how long to remain at a flower before moving on to the next one, the mother blackbird knows how many insects it is best to carry at one time to her young, and the male dung fly knows how long to copulate. A flying insect knows how long to warm its motor before it dares take wing. When it feeds fuel to its muscles and increases its oxygen intake, it spends only the energy needed for takeoff. Every animal lives at its own pace.

So typical of each species are its organs for gathering food that biologists use the organs to classify the species. Teeth, bills, and insect mouthparts; tentacles, talons, and grasping hands; all these and many other food-gathering organs identify the kinship of animals.

Some organs, like the tongue of the anteater and the hand of the giant panda, are incredibly specialized. The anteater, having no teeth at all, feeds with a sticky tongue that can be shoved for 22 inches into a termite mound, then darted in and out 160 times per minute. The panda has an extra "thumb," an extension of the wristbone covered with a pad of skin. The thumb holds the bamboo leaves on which the panda feeds exclusively.

And what is one to make of the archerfish, the sharp-eyed fish that knocks down insects by spitting upon them? It prowls near the surface of the water and, when it sees an insect moving on weeds above its head, squirts a drop or two at the target. It can knock down an insect three feet away. When it aims from below the surface it must compensate for the bending (refraction) of light along its line of vision.

Another predator, the tropical fringe-lipped bat, goes hunting for frogs at dusk. Being familiar with their mating calls, it chooses to strike palatable species instead of poisonous ones and small species instead of those too large to be swallowed.

Archerfish downing a dragonfly

Beaver felling a tree

Beaver and Sea Otter: Aquanauts

Many years ago I was sent by the Forest Service to study beavers in the pine forests of eastern Oregon. Reckless trapping and poaching during the early years of the century had wiped out most of Oregon's beavers, so forest rangers had begun to live-trap a few of the survivors and use them as seed for restoring former colonies.

When two males and two females are planted in a stream they usually hide until nightfall. Come darkness, they cut willow bushes and fell trees for food and construction timbers. I once found a cottonwood tree fully three feet in diameter that had been toppled by a beaver, and I once found the dead body of a beaver—a victim of poor planning—pinned under a tree that he had felled in the wrong direction. With their massive orange-yellow teeth, beavers strip off and eat the sweet inner bark of the fallen trees, meanwhile cutting the branches into short lengths that they will later drag into the stream.

Now they begin to dam the stream. They build the dam of sticks, matted grass, mud, and stones. (On one occasion, I remember, they stole a red lantern from a road-repair site and worked it into their dam.) How they know where to locate the dam is a mystery. Do they judge the slope of the ground by the sound of the stream, whether quiet or noisy? Do they scout around until they find a place where the stream is naturally constricted? Perhaps it's just as well that the answer is unknown, for mystery is part of the beaver's charm.

A pond slowly rises above the new dam and, when it's deep enough to suit the builders, they build a dome-shaped lodge near its center. Here they rest in the daytime, secure from enemies, and here the female will give birth in the following spring to three or four kits.

In preparing for winter the beavers cache piles of green unpeeled sticks on the bottom of the pond. (They do not, as folklore would have it, suck air from the sticks to make them sink!) The piles become refrigerated stores to be drawn upon as needed.

I have great respect for the beaver's ability to build dams and lodges. I have even greater respect for its ability—unique in the animal kingdom—to build *canals*. These are typically about two feet wide and two feet deep; the longest may wind through the forest for hundreds of yards. The beaver uses them for regulating the water level of the pond and for barging sticks to the dam and the lodge.

The beaver is the sole representative of a bloodline thirty million years old. Early on, protobeavers began to manipulate running water. Countless generations later they had grown acutely sensitive to changes in water level. I was impressed with that sensitivity once when I was live-trapping beavers. I had deliberately made a break in a dam and had set a trap upstream in shallow water in the subsiding pond. Predictably, the beavers, alarmed by the drop in the pond's level, came at night to repair the break. But their action brought death to one of their own family. After they had plugged the leak, the water rose and drowned a beaver kit who had earlier wandered into the trap. The adults could not have foreseen the unfortunate consequence of an act that was automatic, as are virtually all wild animal acts.

The beaver's inability to reason—its lack of foresight—is also evident in its habit of felling more trees at a time than it can possibly use. After it has done so, the tree bark dries or molds and becomes inedible. When beavers are newly transplanted to a stand of young aspens they often change it within weeks to a field of jackstraws.

At this point you may sense a contradiction. I had stated earlier that animals tend to be sparing of energy; now I show that a beaver will, on occasion, waste energy in "over-felling." There are two parts to the explanation. First, the beaver's instinct is capable of guiding its behavior only briefly, for periods ranging from seconds to minutes. That instinct is quite incapable of warning him of the future consequences of over-felling. Second, the machinery of instinct often provokes activity beyond the immediate needs of the animal, as an automobile engine often continues to fire a time or two after the ignition has been turned off. Over-felling by the beaver is comparable with the behavior of carnivores known loosely as "the urge to kill." A fox, finding itself in a gull colony or a henhouse, may kill more birds than it can possibly use.

The ocean supports several hundred thousand kinds of plants and cold-blooded animals which, in their turn, provide food for several hundred kinds of warm-blooded birds and mammals. Among the mammals is the sea otter, a creature that lives only in the North Pacific Ocean. The sea otter's manner of feeding and its ability to garner huge amounts of food are unique among carnivores of similar body size. An otter has been known to dive in search of shellfish to sea floors as deep as 318 feet. If an otter finds a thick-shelled clam, abalone, or sea urchin, it may carry the prize to the surface and break it against a rock. Floating belly-up, balancing the rock upon its chest, the otter pounds the food against the rock in repeated blows. Excluding man and his fellow primates, the sea otter is the most skillful and habitual tool-user among mammals.[1]

Living actively the year around in chilly surroundings, the sea otter needs a great deal of food. A fifty-pound individual must eat daily up to one-third of its own weight. (Imagine a fifty-pound boy or girl eating sixteen pounds a day, day after day.) A fifty-pound otter needs daily the food equivalent of 6,000 calories, or more than three times that (1,800 calories) of a growing fifty-pound person. The otter's metabolic rate is three to four times faster than that of a land mammal of similar size.

Because its food income is largely spent in gathering more food and in keeping warm, the otter can't afford to reproduce rapidly. Its single pup, produced once a year or less often, must be suckled for at least six months.

Surviving Without Drinking

Because we feeble animals of the human species respect endurance, we respect it in other animals that manage to survive in harsh surroundings. Consider the oryx, a large African antelope—remarkably adapted to cope with burning winds and drought. It employs many strategies for survival and can survive indefinitely without drinking.[2] Thus,

• It permits its body temperature to rise by twelve degrees Fahrenheit or more before it begins to lose precious moisture through sweating, panting, or simply drying out. After accumulating heat during the day it releases the heat slowly at night.

• Arterial blood supplying the brain is cooled during each intake of breath by a network of fine vessels lying near the back of the throat. As a consequence, body temperature—but not brain temperature—can safely rise to 113 degrees and stay there for as long as eight hours. By contrast, a man will die soon after his deep-body temperature reaches 111 degrees.

• During periods of drought, the skin becomes drier and less permeable to water of evaporation, while body metabolism falls. The oryx "banks its fires" and breathes more slowly, for the quieter its body, the less moisture will pass out in exhaled breath.

• It feeds mainly at night, when the water content of its grassy and shrubby foods is highest. A man surviving a hot day in the desert

Elephant seal with pup

would need five or six times as much water as an oryx of the same body weight.

Marine seals and sea lions, too, are accomplished fasters. All are amphibious, dividing their time between water and land. While in the water they feed; while on land they devote their energies to solving other problems of survival. The elephant seals of the California coast give birth to pups that nurse greedily for about twenty-eight days, then fast without food or drink for up to three months.[3] On Año Nuevo Island, south of San Francisco, I once saw a group of these fat, silvery pups lying like driftwood on the shore, sleeping away the hours as their body fat burned into metabolic water. The ability of elephant seals to fast is an evolutionary gain, an adaptation that allows individuals to devote full time at critical stages of life to whatever they need to be doing—the pups blissfully growing, the mothers nursing, and the fathers copulating, or jousting with rival males.

How Bats and Birds Partition
Their Food Resources

Imagine, now, a young tropical island newly populated with plants
and animals. No bats have reached it yet from the mainland. Several
fruit-eating bats arrive on a favorable wind; they multiply. They are
followed in time by four other kinds of bats that feed, respectively,
on nectar, insects, fresh blood, and fish. The bat fauna is now five-
layered; it demonstrates partitioning of the food resource according
to the feeding strategies of the five species.

This sort of colonization evidently occurred on the Island of Trinidad, eight miles off the coast of South America. Although fourteen,
rather than five, species of bats are now common on Trinidad, they
represent only the five groups that feed on fruit, nectar, insects,
blood, or fish.[4]

The fisherman bats are especially intriguing. They have long,
sharp talons with which they rake minnows from the top of the water. I saw them one evening in Guyana when I was traveling by ca-
noe down a jungle river. They swooped and rose silently in the fad-
ing light, leaving dimpled trails on the water.

Biologist Roderick Suthers once tested the ability of fisherman
bats to locate food by ultrasound echoes—by sonar.[5] He netted several wild bats on their roosts and released them in a large outdoor
cage equipped with a pool. He used a microphone to record the sig-
nals, too shrill for human hearing, uttered by each bat as it prowled
for prey. A high-speed lamp coupled with a camera captured the im-
age of the bat at various stages in its seek-and-destroy missions.
Amazingly, the bat could find and could hit in total darkness a hair-
thin wire projecting less than one-quarter inch above the water. All
the bat needed for orientation was the sound of its own voice bounc-
ing back from this slender target.

Imagine five janitors who clean a large hall and are paid per kilogramme of
trash collected. One janitor uses his hands, one a pitchfork, one a broom,
one a vacuum-cleaner and one a carpet-sweeper. Each janitor is better adapted
than the others to collecting certain trash items, but there are many items

that can be collected by any of several janitors. A good strategy for all janitors is to forage together, thereby constantly assuring themselves of trash-rich areas and avoiding areas partly cleared by other janitors.

This fanciful picture is painted by Jared Diamond to illustrate the sort of partnership which, in the real world, is known as a mixed-species foraging group.[6] Only recently has its full significance been realized. Observers of African grazing animals—the dik dik, duiker, eland, gazelle, hartebeest, impala, springbok, wildebeest, and others—have long known that these species will forage together in various combinations, partitioning the food resource as they travel. And birdwatchers in tropical rainforests have often seen mixed-species flocks moving from tree to tree in a predictable, and evidently purposeful, manner.

It is now clear that mixed-species foraging is routinely practiced by many birds, ungulates, primates, cetaceans, and fishes. But why? What advantage does a bird gain by traveling in a noisy flock? Five theories, not mutually exclusive, are in vogue (Diamond).

• The convoy theory. Grouping offers safety in numbers.

• The gang theory. The larger the group, the more easily it can exploit a local food resource by overwhelming the resident defenders of the resource.

• The beater theory. One species, while foraging, is apt to flush prey that another species can use.

• The pirate theory. One member is often seen snatching food from a fellow-traveler. (If this theory is valid, a chronic loser must, of course, derive compensatory advantages from staying with its group.)

• Feeding efficiency theory. This is essentially the food-partitioning idea, plus the idea that the more members searching, the more likely is one of them to discover food, plus the idea that members learn new feeding techniques from each other.

If further proof is needed that the mixed-species group is a genuine coevolutionary product, it is the fact that the partners in it, while they may represent widely different families, tend to resemble one another in appearance or behavior. They demonstrate social mimicry. Certain New Guinea birds forage together as a brown-and-black flock.[7] Although comprising twenty or more different species, nearly all are reddish brown or black. The flock is led by a babbler (Garritornis), who repeats a distinctive leader call. Several other species in the flock mimic the call, presumably to hold the group together.

The mixed-species pattern illustrates social convergence, with a dash of anatomical convergence. Says Martin Moynihan, a researcher at the Smithsonian Tropical Research Institute, "Individuals of different species which look, sound, or feel alike do tend to interact with one another or with the same 'third parties' more closely or more frequently, on the average, than do individuals of other species which do not resemble one another."[8]

No account of food partitioning would be complete if it failed to mention the New Zealand huia, a bird last seen alive in 1907. Its skill in obtaining food may have led to its doom. It was the world's only avian species in which the bills of the two sexes were very unlike. That of the male was short, straight, and stout; that of the female long, slender, and curved. Male and female huias, traveling in tandem, would search for rotting tree trunks and down logs. Finding

Male and female huias

one, the male would chisel away at promising holes and would expose insect grubs that the female could then seize with her probing bill. By what wordless agreement the two shared the prize can never be known.

Or perhaps the difference in bills evolved as a mechanism insuring that the male and female did not compete too intensely for food. Perhaps the male depended largely on "chiseled" grubs, the female on "pincered" grubs.

It was the huia's misfortune to live in a century when its numbers were steadily falling under attack by Maori and European hunters. Its long black tail feathers, handsomely barred with white, were prized as ornaments. Museum collectors, too, helped to bring the bird's history as a species to an end. But destruction of the forests upon which it depended for food and shelter was surely the mortal stroke. Having specialized so narrowly (compare the manufacturer of buggy whips), the huia could not adapt to a world in which its specialty had lost survival value.

The Parasites

The food specialists supreme in the animal kingdom are the parasites, of which there are many kinds. Ernst Mayr points out that, of the 40,000 species of German animals, no fewer than 10,000 are parasitic on the other 30,000.[9] During their evolution, parasites gave up freedom for security; they now fasten to, or invade the bodies of, larger organisms.

Many have become host-specific; that is, able to survive on only one kind of host. When the great Steller sea-cow of the Bering Sea was exterminated in the 1700s its unique crustacean parasite, a "sea-louse," went with it. The louse would still be unknown had not a few mummified individuals, still clinging to a fragment of sea-cow hide, been discovered by a sharp-eyed curator in the Leningrad Museum.

It's not difficult to imagine how parasitic associations must have evolved. Like the camel who first insinuated his nose, and later his body, into the Arab's tent, a small commensal species would have depended increasingly for nourishment on a larger companion and, after millions of years, would have become an obligate parasite.

Some parasites kill their hosts. The ichneumon wasp lays its egg on a caterpillar and thereby dooms the caterpillar to slow death as the ichneumon's larva chews its way through living tissue. Often in midsummer one can see a tent caterpillar, bearing on its back the white egg of an ichneumon, crawling along in search of a place to spin its cocoon. It will never leave that cocoon.

But most animal parasites do *not* kill their hosts, for it is obviously not in their interest to do so. I suppose that never once have I autopsied a wild carnivore, whether bobcat, skunk, seal, or other species, without finding roundworms, tapeworms, and various other parasites in its body. The carnivores and the parasites are locked in a no-win struggle. The immune defense system of the host keeps the parasites down but never quite out. The host and its parasites represent an entire, though minuscule, balanced ecosystem.

In the annals of South American medicine are records of a most unusual parasite. It is the candiru of the Amazon Basin, a slender, slimy, three-inch catfish that occasionally attacks human bathers.

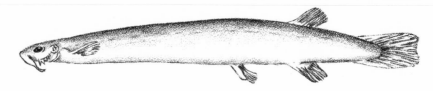

Candiru

Normally a parasite of larger fishes, it fastens to their gills by means of spiny hooks—whereupon it sucks their blood. It is by instinct a crevice-seeker. Hence, young candirus, when only one-sixteenth-inch thick, can penetrate the human ear, nose, urethra, vagina, or anus. Once inside a human body the candiru dies by suffocation, meanwhile erecting its spines. The struggling fish causes intense pain to the bather and must usually be removed surgically. In one case a surgeon had to dissect a woman's bladder to remove a deeply penetrated candiru. And J. R. Norman, of the British Museum (Natural History), recounts the story of a certain Dr. Bach, who "examined natives—a man and three boys—in whom the penis had been amputated as a result of this dreadful accident [penetration by a candiru]."[10]

Ichthyologist Eugene Gudger called the candiru "the only vertebrate parasite of man."[11] He missed the mark, of course, for the little fish does not remain long enough in its host to feed or to reproduce.

How They Meet
Hard Times

W HEN THE HOME OF A WILD ANIMAL becomes too hot or cold, or too wet or dry, or otherwise becomes unlivable, the animal may suspend animation, or move away, or simply lay its eggs in a safe place and die. Its response, being genetically fixed, will vary with the species.

Animal Dropouts

Because microscopic animals can't travel far, most of them meet hard times by dropping out. If you were raised on a farm you will recall that the first rains of autumn resurrected small creatures in many a shallow pond that had baked into dryness under the summer sun. Organisms that enter a death-like state when their habitat becomes unfavorable are cryptobionts (literally, "hidden-life organisms"). They include certain nematode worms, rotifers, and tardigrades.

It is hard to believe that dormant tardigrades can withstand temperatures as high as 308 degrees Fahrenheit (far above the boiling point of water) and as low as minus 459 degrees (near absolute zero). When a specimen of moss that had lain on a dry museum shelf for 120 years was placed in a dish of water, a few tardigrades were seen moving fitfully among its fronds. They died within minutes. We must conclude that even in the dry state they were "alive" in the sense that their metabolism continued at some exceedingly low rate. But metabolism calls for fuel; in this case, stored fuel. Quite possibly they had depleted their fuel to such a level that, once they were placed in water, they could afford only flickering moments of active life.[1]

Whistling swans

But larger animals can't lapse into a deathlike state. If the animal is a vertebrate its heart must continue to pump and its lungs or gills to respire, however slowly. Oxygenated blood must continue to reach its brain.

In the deserts of the American West, Townsend's ground squirrels disappear into their deep subterranean burrows in early summer and reappear in February. They escape the summer's heat by estivating.

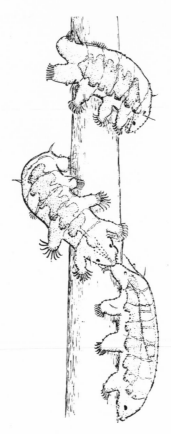

Tardigrades (magnified)

Golden-mantled ground squirrels, living in the mountains, behave contrariwise; they disappear in winter, escaping the cold by hibernating. Black bears, depending on the climate where they live, will hibernate, or will go in and out of hibernation, or will not hibernate at all. (Garrett Hardin tells of a certain Ray Hock who entered the den of a hibernating bear to take its rectal temperature. It was, he mused, "an act of no small courage as it seems to other biologists, whatever might be the thoughts of the bear.")[2]

Once, in midwinter, a farmer brought me a hibernating jumping mouse whose nest he had uncovered while he was plowing. The honey-brown mouse stayed fast asleep in my hand, curled in a tight ball with its face tucked into its groin. It was a thing of geometric beauty. On the following day I carried it indoors to photograph it. Here it slowly stretched for several minutes before it awakened.

And in the Cascade Mountains on a day in May I spied a fresh hole in a snowbank fully three feet deep where a hoary marmot—a Western relative of the woodchuck—had tunneled up to the surface. How had it known, as it slept under three feet of snow, that spring had come? Hibernation involves the setting of an animal's thermostat at a low level in fall and the resetting of it at a higher level in spring.

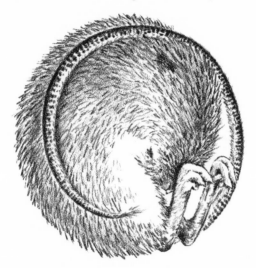

Hibernating jumping mouse

Although the triggering factors for hibernation are imperfectly known, they surely include the amount and kind of fat in the animal's body in spring and again in fall.

While Edmund Jaeger was exploring the Southern California desert in December 1946, he was startled to find a poorwill—a bird related to swifts—hibernating in a rocky crevice.[3] His discovery made quite a stir, for until then no bird had been known to hibernate. Although its body was cold the bird slowly opened its eyes when it was disturbed. Poorwills are insect eaters. Hibernation for as long as three months is their unique way of surviving when insects are scarce.

In the winter of 1972–73, Mexican commercial fishermen learned a secret long known to the Seri Indians—that green turtles overwinter on the bottom of the Sea of Cortez.[4] These air-breathing creatures submerge in waters fifty feet deep or deeper during the coldest months of winter. How they get oxygen remains unexplained.

Certain very small warm-blooded animals are faced with hardship every twenty-four hours, for at night they lose body heat rapidly and can't restore it by feeding in the dark. The Old World bamboo bat and the bee hummingbird, each weighing less than a copper cent, survive by entering torpor during the hours when they are unable to feed. The bee hummingbird, smallest of birds, perches at night like a stone and allows its body heat to fall. By doing so it saves about one-third the energy it would otherwise lose.

Hibernation is both mysterious and disturbing. It borders on trance and hypnosis, though is scarcely more mysterious than the ordinary sleep into which we nightly fall. In sleep we travel alternately through utter blackness and through realms where unreal objects seem believably real. We dip into unused pockets of memory. And if we try deliberately to postpone sleep we are overruled in the end by brain cells beyond our control.

Prolonged research on the meaning of sleep has failed to explain it satisfactorily. Does sleep give our body cells time to repair the damage they suffered while at work during the day? Is it merely "the innocent sleep . . . that knits up the ravell'd sleave of care"? Or is it a legacy from hominid ancestors who resorted to sleep during darkness, when they could neither hunt nor gather and when it was unsafe for them to be roaming about?

Many wild mammals sleep approximately as we do. At any rate, their brain-waves during sleep resemble ours. Even earthworms learn their way through a laboratory maze more quickly at night, when they are normally awake, than during the day, when they are normally asleep. But how is one to explain the least shrew that daily must hunt down and consume prey equivalent to its own body weight? Can it *afford* to sleep? And what of the sooty tern that spends weeks continuously in the air above the tropical Pacific Ocean?

Rites of Passage: The Mystery of Migration

Many animals meet hard times by migrating. Their seasonal movements are governed by changes in the environment, as well as by the internal clocks or calendars that all animals are thought to possess. The caribou of Alaska and the wildebeests of Africa, the gray whales and fur seals of the North Pacific Ocean, many ducks, geese, and songbirds, monarch butterflies, ladybird beetles, and thousands of other species migrate. More than a hundred million birds leave northwestern America every fall.

Migration is specific and largely instinctive. Originating long ago, it can be thought of as "fossilized behavior." Profound changes over the face of the earth including movements of continental ice, the rising and falling of sea levels, mountain building, and continental drift were doubtless responsible for setting in motion the migratory patterns that exist today.

Every migratory bird knows from the moment of hatching a great deal about migration; the rest it learns by watching older birds. But what are we to make of the monarch butterfly that completes only one migration (of about 2,500 miles round-trip) before it dies? Monarch generations are distinct. "The individual butterflies that fly south in the fall are several generations removed from their ancestors that flew north the previous spring," explains Lincoln Brower.[5] Thus, no young monarch can conceivably learn from its elders, and yet year after year monarchs travel from the United States and Canada to the same wintering places in central Mexico, and even to the same trees.

And why do no land-breeding birds of the South Temperate Zone move to the North Temperate Zone for wintering? Mystery upon mystery.

Although man's interest in bird migration goes back for centuries, only recently—with the aid of aircraft and electronic instruments— has migration been revealed as a truly amazing performance. Biologists who radar-tracked birds flying at night above Cape Cod recorded blips at altitudes up to 20,000 feet.[6] Earlier, climbers on

Mount Everest had been startled to see yellow-billed choughs at 27,000 feet and to see bar-headed geese flying *above* the summit of the mountain, above 29,000 feet.[7]

The arctic tern is the champion of long-distance travelers. It nests to within 600 miles of the North Pole. After the young terns have hatched and have learned to fly they follow their parents to Antarctica. Some terns evidently circle the whole Southern Ocean, returning to their northern breeding grounds after twenty-three months and a pilgrimage of 14,000 miles. This means that they enjoy continuous daylight for eight months of the year.

A birdwatcher flying one day in a small plane over San Francisco Bay was overtaken and passed by two flocks of migrating sandpipers. He glanced at the plane's speedometer, saw that he was doing ninety

Laysan albatross

miles an hour, and estimated that the birds were doing a hundred and ten. (Perhaps an exaggerated estimate, though still very fast.) "The two flocks," he reported, "were in close echelon, the individual positions, fixed, the wing-beats rhythmic and powerful."[8]

The unprotected human face could not long endure the pressure and chill-factor of air moving at a hundred and ten miles per hour. Man will never match the sandpiper's performance; he can only marvel at it.

In 1957 two of my friends, Karl Kenyon and Dale Rice, took eighteen albatrosses from their nests on Midway Island and shipped them by air to widely scattered points in the North Pacific.[9] The birds, rigged with identification bands, were then set free. Would they return to Midway? The men waited. Fourteen birds *did* come home; four were never seen again. One had flown 4,120 miles from the Philippines in 32.1 days, while another had flown 3,200 miles from Washington State in 10.1 days at an average speed of 317 miles per day.

Two things are remarkable about the homing of these birds: they

Ruby-throated hummingbird

found their way unerringly across a trackless sea, and they traveled thousands of miles at a season when albatrosses do not normally migrate and do not have the energy stores (fat deposits) of migrating birds.

The energy cost of migrating is critical; it can mean the difference between life and a tragic death. The ruby-throated hummingbird must cross the Gulf of Mexico in a nonstop flight of more than five hundred miles on fuel weighing less than one gram (0.035 ounce). To be sure, the bird waits for a tailwind before it takes off.[10]

The Map Sense of Birds

Biologists have long tried to discover how a bird knows the correct migratory route of its species. What hidden landmarks and seamarks guide it to a destination it may never have seen? A classic experiment in the 1950s designed to reveal the map sense of birds was carried out by a German, Franz Sauer. Early in the course of the experiment he wrote:

We had hatched and raised [lesser whitethroat] warblers in completely closed, soundproof chambers where they lived in the illusion of eternal summer, year in and year out. Yet, although they had no outward cues of the yearly rhythm of nature, in the autumn the birds would begin to flit restlessly from branch to branch or flutter continually over their perches, night after wakeful night. They kept this up for many weeks—about the length of time it would have taken to fly to Africa.[11]

So Sauer placed one bird at a time on the floor of a planetarium, where it could see an artificial night sky preset to a certain date and geographic location. The bird would take up many positions as it hopped about in its cage, though always favoring the one that the stars told it was southeast, toward Africa.

The next spring, when his birds again grew restless, he repeated the experiment. Now the birds favored a *northwest* position; they were keen on returning to central Europe. He was forced to conclude that warblers can navigate by the stars!

To prove it he played a trick on a bird called Johnny. He shifted the planetarium stars to indicate a position several hundred miles east of the true one. "The bird at once showed that it was deeply disturbed. It looked excitedly at the unfamiliar sky and for almost a full minute stood irresolutely. Then it suddenly turned and took wing in the opposite direction. According to the sky, its position at the moment corresponded to a point near Lake Balkhash in Siberia; Johnny, to correct its displacement, was heading directly toward the usual migration starting point in Germany!"[12]

Stephen Emlen, an American ornithologist, used indigo buntings in similar star-sense experiments.[13] He worked under both real and planetarium skies. To spare himself tedious hours counting bird hops, he arranged a circular cage so that each bird undergoing a test stood on an ink-pad at the center of the circle. When it hopped, trying to reach the sky, it landed on a sloping sheet of white paper, where it left its footprints. It then dropped back to the center. The result was a permanent record of the number of landings per hour per compass direction. When the night sky was hidden by clouds, real or artificial, his birds became disoriented. They "boxed the compass," leaving footprints at random around the circular cage.

Emlen pursued similar studies year after year, at times with normal birds and at other times with birds that he had fooled, by artificial lighting, into supposing that spring was fall. Fooled males developed bright-blue breeding plumage in midwinter. And he projected on the dome of the planetarium a false pattern of stars rotating around a "North Star." He concluded that, in buntings at least,

• Young birds respond to the apparent rotation of stars around the Pole. "The stars near the North Star move through much smaller arcs than the stars near the celestial equator, and this enables the young birds to determine a north-south directional axis."[14] As they mature, the birds learn to orient accurately by star pattern alone, even when the pattern is motionless, as when "frozen" on the planetarium sky.

• Star patterns tell only north and south; they don't provide the bird with a map. That is, buntings lack the precise time sense which, along with star sense, they would need for estimating latitude.

• Although they fly in opposite directions in spring and fall, they fix on the same northern constellations. Shifting ratios of two hor-

Stars moving around the Pole Star (time exposure)

mones in the blood evidently reverse the bird's polarity. When hormone A is dominant, the bird thinks that its goal lies in the north;
when hormone B is dominant, it thinks the opposite.

Other biologists studied pigeons fitted with frosted contact lenses.
Now the birds could see objects only within a distance of a few
yards. Still, when they were carried into the countryside as far as

eighty miles from their loft, most of them returned. One of the biologists wrote that "it was a remarkable experience. The birds arrived very high overhead and fluttered down to a landing in the fields around the loft. Being unable to see the loft, they waited for us to pick them up and carry them the last few feet."[15] They depended largely on their geomagnetic sense of direction—that remarkable sense possessed by certain bacteria, flatworms, molluscs, insects, sharks, salamanders, birds, mice, and porpoises.

By means of other elegant experiments, ornithologists have shown that birds live in a sensory world very different from ours. Birds find their way to distant places by sensing environmental changes to which we are blind and deaf or to which we respond unconsciously. Birds are sensitive to polarized and ultraviolet light, to low-frequency sounds (such as those produced by jet streams in the upper air and by distant surf), to atmospheric pressure, and to magnetic lines of force. Add the ability to recognize ordinary visual and audible signs such as those that humans can also recognize, and you will agree that birds come into the world equipped with a broad panel of orientation instruments.

I don't mean that every bird possesses all the foregoing instruments. Warbler and bunting brains, for instance, are not known to contain crystals of magnetite like those in the brain of the pigeon. I mean only that Nature seems forever to be testing throughout the animal kingdom a wide variety of compass systems.

Birds knew the shape of the world before Magellan . . . before Columbus . . . before Man. All the principal threads of natural selection and adaptation are woven into bird migration. If you would know these threads you would do nearly as well to study bird migration by itself as to study the whole world of nature.

Migration on Wheels

Janice Mather, a British biologist, not satisfied with the folk notion that wheel-running by caged hamsters, squirrels, mice, and rats is purely a response to boredom, set out recently to find a deeper meaning.[16] The wheel-running urge is indeed a powerful instinct; it may lead a rat to cover twenty-seven miles around and around in a single day. Mather found her first clue in published reports on wheel-running by starved laboratory rats. These run more actively than do well-fed ones, which suggests that caged animals search (as Mather puts it) for "the missing resource"—in this case food and drink. Moreover, females in heat run more actively than do juveniles, or pregnant adults, or very old postmenopausal adults, which suggests that sexual pleasure can be a missing resource. And, not surprisingly, population crowding alone will cause animals to step up their use of activity wheels.

Mouse in laboratory wheel

To test whether *home* can also be a missing resource, Mather and a colleague, Robin Baker, took British wood mice from the forest and placed them in a room that allowed the mice a choice of four activity wheels oriented to the four quarters of the compass.[17] In significant numbers the mice selected the wheels that promised to take them home. They followed their magnetic sense of direction.

Mather and Baker believe that, although wheel-running can be triggered by more than one factor, it basically reflects the animal's urge to travel, either to remove itself from the immediate area or to search for specific resources. It is "exploratory migration."

How remote and strange and subterranean are the roots of migratory behavior!

How They
Defend Themselves

EVERY WILD ANIMAL CALLS UPON UNIQUE STRATEGIES for protection against enemies and rivals. The tortoise and the porcupine rely on tough or spiny armaments. The weapon of the skunk is no secret. The rabbit has large eyes and ears like radar antennae that give early warning of a stalking fox and, even if surprised, the rabbit will usually escape by clever footwork. And all animals know the value of concealment; when faced with danger they act first to become invisible.

Venoms

Some animals rely for defense on elaborate venoms that they deliver by means of spines, spurs, hollow teeth, tentacles, or special guns. The bombardier beetle carries a science-fiction weapon—a turret-shaped segment on the rear end of its body that can be aimed like a cannon. A chamber within the beetle's abdomen manufactures two chemicals, hydroquinone and hydrogen peroxide. When the beetle is threatened it opens a valve that allows the chemicals to enter a second, strong-walled chamber, where they mix with enzyme catalysts. *Pop*! The foul-smelling, irritating mixture explodes, spurting from the cannon in a boiling hot mist that usually repels the threatening ant, spider, or other enemy. If the enemy forces the issue, the beetle reloads and continues to fire about six shots a minute until it runs out of ammunition. Fate decides whether the attacker gains a meal or only a rude education.

Some anti-evolutionists argue that natural selection could never have produced a weapon as complex as that of the bombardier. At all incomplete stages, they insist, the weapon would have been so much useless baggage to be lugged around—and Nature does not waste energy. Moreover, they ask, Would not the primitive ancestral beetle, while perfecting its weapon, have blown itself to bits? Chris Weber, a computer programmer, answers the question.

There's no problem explaining where the hydroquinone and the hydrogen peroxide come from. . . . Hydrogen peroxide is a normal metabolic product in insects, and various quinones are used to harden the cuticle of insects. All kinds of insects therefore secrete these chemicals. As a by-product, hydroquinone tastes bad to predators and is the chemical that makes stink bugs stink. So, if an insect's cuticle became indented, forming little sacs to store some of this hydroquinone, it would have an advantage over its fellows even if its storage mechanism was not yet very efficient.[1]

Bombardier beetle

Evolutionists and anti-evolutionists have been debating for more than a century the likelihood that natural selection could have created (in Darwin's words) such "organs of extreme perfection and complication" as the bombardier's cannon.[2] The debate is still with us, despite the fact that biologists have in the meanwhile discovered and described thousands of intermediate structures that shed light on the stages through which organs of extreme perfection might have passed during their evolution. (I'm reminded of a Scottish expression, a blunt reply to a kibitzer who questions the worth of a job still in progress: "Never show a fool a thing half done.")

Many snakes are venomous, as are also a few other reptiles (including Arizona's gila monster), a few mammals, but no birds. Purely by chance, it would seem, venoms are unevenly distributed.

Snake venoms are of four chemical types, not all produced by the same species. One venom may paralyze the nerves of the heart and lungs, a second may destroy blood-vessel walls (thus bringing circulation to a halt), a third may destroy red cells in the blood, and a fourth may cause the blood to coagulate.

Venoms are used variously for defense, for offense, and for obtaining food. A rattlesnake bites when it's threatened by a predator and it bites to paralyze the rodents and lizards upon which it feeds. Interestingly, when a rattlesnake has ambushed and struck a mouse it does not give the *coupe de grâce* right away but allows the victim to wander off. Within minutes, the snake begins to track with deadly precision, flicking its tongue in and out to taste the lingering scent of the mouse and the scent of its own discharged venom. It soon reaches the mouse, by now dead or dying and in a condition to be easily swallowed.

In 1957, a world expert on snakes, after he was bitten on the thumb by a twenty-six-inch African boomslang, kept sufficiently cool to write down for the benefit of science the last symptoms he was able to describe. Karl P. Schmidt, then curator of zoology at Chicago's Field Museum, went home after the accident, and experienced "strong chill and shaking . . . bleeding from gums . . . blood in urine . . . violent nausea and vomiting." He began to breathe so loudly that his labored efforts could be heard all over the house. He died twenty-four hours after being bitten.[3]

Only two groups of *warm-blooded* animals are venomous and both are holdovers from Mesozoic time. Is there perhaps some biological meaning here? Do these forms "remember" their reptilian ancestry?

In the first group are shrews of worldwide distribution, some of which are certainly, and others probably, venomous. The best known is the short-tailed shrew of eastern North America. A nervous little creature only three to four inches long, it hunts among dead leaves and topsoil for beetles, grubs, worms, slugs, snails, and mice. It pro-

Pacific rattlesnake

duces a salivary venom which, if injected by bite, can kill small animals and cause lingering pain to humans.

In the second group of venomous mammals—the monotremes—are the duckbilled platypus of Australia and the echidnas of Australia, Tasmania, and New Guinea. These primitive creatures have hair and milk-glands, but lay eggs. Male monotremes have a sharp, horny spur, positioned like a cowboy's spur, on each ankle. The spur is hollow and carries a liquid secreted by a gland in the leg. Although the liquid produced by the platypus is venomous, the one produced by the echidnas is not certainly so. A veil of mystery still surrounds the biology of these curious animals.

"One healthy man who was spurred by a captive platypus," writes Ernest Walker, "fell to the ground in intense pain; his hand and arm became greatly swollen, and he suffered for months from the poison in his system."[4] The platypus is evidently not immune to its own venom, for "one male attacked his mate in captivity, driving his spurs into her flanks; the female nearly died as a result."[5]

Because spurs develop only in *male* monotremes, they are perhaps used mainly when males fight with rivals for the possession of females. Doubtless they are also used in defense against predators. Native cats (marsupials), the wedge-tailed eagle, and the diamond python may still prey on the platypus, while the Tasmanian devil and the Tasmanian wolf, both now extinct on the Australian continent, may have preyed on it in the recent past.

Mysterious Poisons

Whereas venoms harm by being injected, poisons harm by being ingested. Several hundred species of tropical marine fishes are deadly poisonous—some always so and some occasionally, and unpredictably, so. Eating puffer (globe fish) in Japan, says physician Bruce Halstead, is like playing Russian roulette.[6] The poisons of marine fishes and invertebrates are complex and mysterious. Some harmful species become poisonous by eating poisonous plankton or seaweed. After feeding on red-tide plankton, a clam or mussel will become poisonous to warm-blooded animals, including humans, while itself remaining unaffected.

The clam does not "intend" to kill; it gains nothing by being poisonous and hence its poison must be regarded as an evolutionary by-product. But the poisons of the puffer and many of its tropical companions, being nearly always present, are presumably evolutionary adaptations for defense.

The evolutionary meaning of *plant* poisons in relation to animals can also be mystifying. I once lived for several months on the tropical island of Grand Cayman, where I was cautioned by the natives never to taste the attractive yellow fruit of the manchineel tree nor even to touch its leaves. It is one of the most toxic plants in tropical

America. What is mystifying is that if the fruit is eaten by a human it causes stomach ulceration, sloughing of the gut lining, and even slow death, while if eaten by reptiles and birds it is digested without ill effect.

The point is, what does the manchineel gain by bearing fruit that is attractive and at the same time poisonous? Why should the manchineel "try" to kill those animals that might disperse its seeds? Part of the answer may be this—the manchineel coevolved with reptiles (such as iguanas and tortoises) and birds (such as parrots and doves) over a time sufficient for these fruit-eaters to have developed immunity to its poison. Man, a newcomer to the environment, has not yet gained immunity. What is called for now are feeding trials involving the animals that safely ingest manchineel fruit, coupled with physiological studies of their digestive systems.

But the main question—Why was the manchineel fruit poisonous in the first place?—is still open. E. J. H. Corner, Cambridge University botanist, suggests that when the first fleshy fruits were evolving in tropical forests they were concurrently being attacked by many kinds of animals. (And often, I presume, before the fruits were ripe and capable of dispersing their seeds via animals.) Corner proposes that "simple camouflage of the fruit and mechanical protection gave place to distastefulness and poisons, as visual and manipulative acuity [of the animals] increased, and some of these poisons came to permeate the plants."[7] The plants under attack coevolved in both chemical structure and in outward form with the animals that attacked them.

Gentler Methods of Defense

Most animals do not defend themselves with special weapons but simply count on avoiding notice, or on practicing deceit. Passive defense is biologically the cheapest. An animal that can spend its calories on feeding and reproducing is better off than one that must also spend calories on poison weaponry, a protective shell, or an obnoxious odor.

Mice and most other small mammals venture from their dens only at night. Rabbits freeze in their tracks at the sight of a dog. When an opossum is attacked by a fox it fakes death, closes its eyes and falls limply to the ground, "playing possum." If the fox is not hungry it walks away, its mental releasers of attack blocked by the sight of a passive catch, while the opossum escapes to breed others of its "stupid" sort.

When I visit the Alaskan tundra in summer I occasionally flush a rock sandpiper from her nest. She flies a few yards, then staggers, drops one wing, and cries piteously. Oh, what suffering! Surely she is crippled. If I were a fox she would draw me on—though always *just* out of reach—until she would miraculously recover and fly away. Not being a fox but an inquisitive biologist, I start walking in ever widening circles around the spot where I first flushed the bird until I spy her moss-lined nest.

When herring are moving toward their spawning grounds they run in schools extending for as long as seventeen miles and containing millions of fish.[8] The schooling of herring and other fishes is primarily a defense strategy based on safety in numbers. Schooling is characteristic of species that live in open water or where hiding places are scarce, and is more prevalent in daylight than in darkness. A typical school moving through the water will form, disperse, and reform without following a leader. When the school is under attack by a predator, the individuals on the outside are the first ones to be picked off. Thus the instinct to school is reinforced by the tendency of individuals to centralize, to keep the school compact. And the instinct is surely successful, for about 16,000 of the 20,000 known species of fish display it at one time or another during their life cycle.

A few years ago, biologists at a Scottish marine laboratory posed the question, How do individuals maintain position in the school? That is, how do they swim polarized and synchronized? To find out, they brought twenty-five saithe (a codlike fish) into an aquarium and tested the ability of blindfolded individuals to school. After wandering aimlessly for a while, all were able to do so. "We believe," concluded the biologists, "that the sensory input used by blinded fish to maintain position . . . is [through] the lateral organ."[9]

They had confirmed a long-standing theory that the lateral line—a faint row of dots along each side of nearly all fishes—is sensitive to

Schooling fishes

low-frequency vibrations. It functions between touch and hearing. The bow wave, or shock wave, created by a fish moving through the water carries a message to others in the school. Whereas humans marching in a parade depend on sight to maintain individual distance, fishes depend largely on infrasound hearing.

The white coats of Alaskan animals are not white for the same reason. Snow-matching white is a *defensive* adaptation for the collared lemming, arctic hare, and ptarmigan, but an *offensive* adaptation for the arctic fox, polar bear, and snowy owl. Camouflaged hunters stalk camouflaged prey.

Protective coloration is the sole defense for most of the world's 700,000 species of insects. Hopelessly inferior in size to their back-

Polar bear

boned enemies, the insects survive through concealment. A classic example is furnished by the peppered moth of Britain.[10] Before 1849, collectors knew it as a light-colored, speckled species that blended almost perfectly with the pale, lichen-splotched bark of the trees where it rested. Nature had camouflaged it. In 1849, near Manchester, a single black variant of the moth was collected; by 1900, about 98 percent of the Manchester moths were black. What agent could have brought about such a rapid change in the ratio of blacks to grays?

During the latter half of the nineteenth century the human population of Britain was growing rapidly, along with the volume of coal burned in homes and factories. Soon it was the black moth resting on the bark of the soot-blackened tree that was the less conspicuous variant. Fewer blacks than grays were eaten by birds; hence more blacks survived to tip the ratio in favor of their genetic kind. The people of Manchester had unwittingly carried out a test of the speed with which natural selection, given opportunity, can act.

The Imitators

Butterflies are fragile, and many gain protection by specializing in deceit. When monarch butterflies in winter are clinging by the thousands to their hibernation trees they might be thought vulnerable to insect-eating birds, but in fact most of them are unpalatable. A bird that eats a monarch, falls ill, and vomits, rarely needs a second lesson in butterfly identification.

So the viceroy butterfly (a very distantly related species) mimics the monarch. Although the viceroy happens to be edible, the birds avoid it anyway. It has become a "sheep in wolf's clothing." The birds seem never to learn that a "monarch" sporting a black line on the hind wings is actually a viceroy and is edible.

Monarch, viceroy, and queen

Another mimic of the monarch is the queen butterfly. Strangely, though, the queen is as noxious as the species it imitates. Here mimicry is not intended to deceive the bird but to warn it off. A young bird that attacks monarchs will soon learn to avoid *both* monarchs and queens. Mimicry in this case reduces the likelihood that an individual monarch or an individual queen will lose its life.

And mimicry in the monarch has a still more curious dimension. Given a choice, a female monarch will lay her eggs on a milkweed plant, for it is the bitter chemicals (cardenolides) in the sap that carry through the tissues of the monarch's caterpillar to protect the adult from birds. But if the female is obliged to lay her eggs on a non-bitter plant such as a cabbage, her offspring will be edible. Of course the birds can't know this, with the result that the cabbage-reared monarch becomes a harmless "automimic" of its own unpalatable relatives.

When biologists speak of mimicry they honor the memory of two explorers who collected butterflies in tropical South America while Darwin was still alive. The men were Henry Walter Bates and Fritz Müller. So, a butterfly or other animal that gains immunity from attack by imitating an unpalatable species is called a Batesian mimic. (Example, the viceroy.) One that *is* unpalatable and gains immunity by resembling other unpalatables is called a Müllerian mimic. (Example, the queen.)[11]

It can easily be shown that mimicry is more than a pretty theory—that it does indeed have survival value to the species that adopts it. Jane Brower carried out an experiment in central Florida involving eight captive jays and about a thousand butterflies.[12] The birds—Florida scrub jays—may have had experience in the wild with monarchs, which visit the scene of the experiment in winter and spring, but not with viceroys, which stay farther north. Brower designated four jays as Experimentals and four as Controls.

To the Experimentals she offered live monarchs. After they had tasted one or two they did not, during any later trial, eat another monarch or even touch one. After fifty trials she began occasionally to substitute a viceroy (the mimic) for a monarch (the model). The birds rejected the mimic as they had the model. Moreover, they remembered to do so after an interval of two weeks, during which time no butterflies of any kind were on the menu.

To the Controls she offered only viceroys, which the birds ate without hesitation. Q. E. D.

All very neat, you may think, but how can a monarch promote its bloodline if, to educate a bird, it must sacrifice its own life? What good can the mortal lesson bring? John Alcock answers the question. "If the monarch has to die, at least it may be increasing the odds that some individuals with shared genes will survive to reproduce because they will be avoided by the educated predator."[13]

So the monarch dies for a genetic reason—to further the reproductive success of its kin. It does *not* die out of thoughtfulness—to benefit others at calculated cost to itself.

Philosophy aside, the ongoing wars of strategy between birds and butterflies illustrate how wild animals campaign unceasingly for survival; how they move and countermove on fields teeming with enemies, allies, and neutrals. Rarely is a campaign so simple that its manoeuvres can clearly be seen and its outcome predicted. Biologists, though, will continue to study these campaigns for the pure wonders they generate and for the delightful surprises that time and again they provide.

Many years ago I worked as a summer ranger in Mount Ranier National Park, where I often heard the high-pitched calls of hoary marmots, locally known as whistlers. The calls pierced the clear alpine air and echoed from the cliffs. They were provoked by the sudden appearance in a marmot colony of a person, a weasel, a golden eagle, or other potential predator. Although I supposed them to be alarm calls warning other marmots of impending danger, I did not realize that they were also expressions of animal "altruism." Any marmot that cries alarm may draw attention to itself and thus increase its own risk of being killed.

Zoologist Paul Sherman and students from the University of California recently explored the roots of alarm calling in Belding's ground squirrels at Tioga Pass.[14] These animals lift their heads and give a shrill call at the first sign of danger. Using hair dye and ear tags, the experimenters marked individual squirrels, and they marked the squirrels' dens with stakes and painted rocks. At one time or another during the experiment they knew the ages and the familial relationships, through the maternal line, of more than a thousand squirrels.

The experiment was designed to answer this question: Does a

squirrel living within earshot of relatives cry alarm more readily than one living near squirrels that are unrelated (or are not known to be related)? In other words, does the average squirrel practice "nepotism," putting itself at greater risk for a relative than for a nonrelative?

The experimenters camped near the Tioga Pass colony for three summers, piling up 3,082 hours of observation. They carefully recorded 102 interactions between predators (weasels, badgers, dogs, coyotes, and martens) and known-age, known-sex squirrels. They learned that, when a predator appears, adult and yearling female squirrels give alarm calls *more* frequently than would be expected if calls were at random, while males regardless of age give alarm calls *less* frequently. They also learned that young males permanently emigrate from their birthplaces before they are a year old, and that adult males often wander between breeding seasons. Thus a male is less likely than a female to encounter relatives. Moreover, it is doubtful that a male knows his own offspring or remembers his sexual contacts with various females.

"Warning relatives," concluded Sherman, "is a likely function of the alarm call that Belding's ground squirrels give when terrestrial predators approach."[15] The tendency to cry alarm is evidently linked not only with the caller's sex but with the caller's recognition of its extended family.

Sociobiology

Edward O. Wilson, in his book *Sociobiology: The New Synthesis*, proposes that the disciplines of animal behavior and animal ecology (in relation to evolutionary thought) be combined and codified to form the discipline of sociobiology, which would be the systematic study of all forms of social behavior in both animals and humans.[16] Sociobiology deserves, he says, equal rank with two older disciplines: molecular biology and developmental biology. He continues:

The central theoretical problem of sociobiology [is] how can altruism, which by definition reduces personal fitness, possibly evolve by natural selection? The answer is kinship: if the genes causing the altruism are shared by two organisms because of common descent, and if the altruistic act by one organism increases the joint contribution of these genes to the next generation, the propensity to altruism will spread through the gene pool.[17]

Similar explanations of animal altruism predate Wilson and have been widely accepted. Some biologists, though, claim that Wilson goes too far when he suggests that human animals, like nonhuman animals, have *genes* for altruism. They claim that his concept of human behavior is deterministic. They claim that if an undesirable tendency, such as one toward aggression, can be shown to be inherent, it may be judged by the general public to be immutable and even good. But genes for aggression have been identified in nonhuman animals, so why not presume that they exist in humans? And genes for intelligence have been identified in humans, so why not postulate human genes for altruism?

What Wilson meant to say, and did say, was that environment plays the major part in shaping human behavior, yet genes play their own part, even if indirectly. There *are* genetic components to human action. This is not to deny that cultural evolution based on teaching and learning largely determines our individual personalities and our collective human character. Far removed from other beasts by our culture, we now hear only fitfully the animal voices of our ancestors. We hear only faintly what zoologist David Barash calls "the whisperings within."[18]

Wilson is trying to organize and promote sociobiology, and I believe we ought to wish him well. We can surely agree that to find through sociobiological research the answers to evolutionary questions will be difficult. I'm not aware that a gene for any behavior (as distinct from an anatomical structure) has yet been isolated. While it is rather easy to map the locus on a fruit fly chromosome of the gene for mutant *white-eye*, it will be much harder to map the locus on the chromosome of the mother sandpiper of the altruistic gene for *cripple act.*

How They Breed

THE GREATER COMPLEXITY OF A MAN than a bacterium is the result of a momentous happening a billion years ago, when life was still microbial. Certain individuals began to fuse with others of similar kind to exchange genetic information. Then, neither as male nor female but as "differents," they parted. Mixis, or the union of sexual cells, or mating, was evolving. Mixis increased the possibility of new genetic combinations, of new individuals or selves. The roots of the great Tree of Life were spreading. A world populated up to now by colorful slimes and drifting particles was on its way to producing a Leonardo da Vinci.

Seaworms, Tumblebugs, and Starfishes

Nature has tested a myriad reproductive strategies, one of which is the spawning dance of the palolo worms in shallow waters of the tropical South Pacific Ocean. In 1899, Harvard zoologist Alexander Agassiz described "the rising of the seaworms" after watching them swarm so thickly as to resemble vermicelli soup.[1] Their dance is exquisitely timed with daily, lunar, and annual cycles of the moon. The main performance lasts only a few hours, beginning at daybreak at neap tide at the third quarter of the October-November moon. Native fishermen anticipate it and are ready with nets to gather the worms for food.

Remarkably, only the hind end, or stolon, of each worm takes part in the ritual. Breaking loose from the body proper, it rises to the surface, tail foremost and writhing furiously. About half the stolons are loaded with eggs and half with sperms. In the frenzy of the dance the

Giant slugs

stolons rupture and shed their products at random into the sea where, in the dawn, floating eggs are fertilized by floating sperms. A loveless mating, yet beautiful in its way.

One amazing feature of the dance is that the stolon, though brainless and sightless, is strongly attracted to light, whereas the body proper is repelled by it. After the stolon ruptures it dies, while the body slowly regenerates a new stolon for the next year's performance.

Whereas every ocean sunfish abandons a million eggs in the open sea, every tumblebug, or scarab beetle, lays one egg at a time but carefully attempts to insure its future. Male and female beetles, working together, roll animal dung into a ball and tumble it down a pit they have excavated. Then the female lays a single egg on the ball. The two beetles cover it lightly with earth. When the egg hatches, its larva will feast on the dung.

There's a parallel, I think, between the behavior of the beetle, burying a bit of itself toward immortality, and the behavior of the Egyptian pharaoh digging a tomb toward the same end. Of the two rituals, that of the beetle makes more sense.

So dependent is evolution on both pinball chance and opportunism that we might expect at least a few species, among the billions that have evolved, to have joined in commensal or symbiotic associations for the purpose of reproduction. And so they have. Witness the austral caddisfly-and-starfish combination. Caddisfly larvae are the soft-bodied grubs, well known to anglers, that cling to the undersides of stones in brooks and lakes, protected within neat tubular houses that they build from sand grains or slivers of wood. They never leave their houses until, as adults, they molt, crawl from the water, and take wing.

Two biologists who were studying marine life along the New Zealand coast were surprised to find that many starfishes contained caddisfly eggs.[2] They were surprised, first, because few insects of any kind can tolerate salt water, and second, because the tough, armor-studded body of a starfish is hardly the place one would expect a female caddisfly to select for a nursery. But the austral caddisfly does, in fact, search for a starfish exposed at low tide, then oviposits through one of the small pores on the animal's back. The eggs incubate for about five weeks, when the newly hatched larvae escape from their prison by some unknown route and begin to feed on seaweed.

Here is a pure example of commensalism; the starfish as host and the insect as tolerated guest. But how did the arrangement get started? The caddisfly's trick is as improbable as that of the tropical mosquito which lays its egg on its foot, then shoves the foot through a wormhole in a bamboo shoot containing rainwater![3]

A Lifelong Attachment

An extreme mode of sexual togetherness is displayed by certain deep-sea anglerfishes, the males of which live parasitically attached to the females.[4] Until the 1920s it was supposed that small fishes seen clinging to the bodies of much larger specimens were simply the young of the larger ones. Then it became clear that the "young"

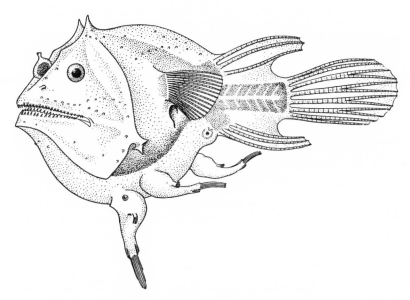

Female anglerfish with male parasites

were fully adult males, grossly deformed. Ichthyologists of the British Museum (Natural History) described a female 40.1 inches (1,030 mm) long from which there dangled a 3.1-inch (80 mm) male.[5] The female would have outweighed the male perhaps two thousand to one.

In the larval stage, the male anglerfish is free-swimming, nearly transparent, and toothless. Somehow he finds a mate in the black waters a mile or more deep—doubtless by trailing her scent—and fastens to her body, where he is doomed to spend the rest of his life. The attachment site is haphazard; it may be almost anywhere on her body between belly and forehead. He matures into a dwarf having degenerate eyes, nostrils, and mouth. While his jaws fuse with her skin, his gills and heart continue to function; they provide him with vital oxygen. One might expect the female's tissues to reject those of the male as being "foreign," but in fact the grafting of the two individuals proceeds without a hitch. As many as four males may attach to the same female. It is thought that the hormone produced by the female when she releases her eggs triggers the release of sperms from all her consorts at once—but no one knows for certain.

The sexual arrangement of the anglerfish is an uncommon sort of parasitism, for its net effect is beneficial rather than harmful. It is an alliance in which the male unwittingly sacrifices his identity and freedom for the long-term good of his race. He becomes simply the female's "testicle in residence."

The family Ceratioidea, of which the parasitic anglerfish is a member, contains nearly one hundred species. Some of them behave sexually like most fishes; their males are independent. Others once thought to be parasitic are evidently not so. They slowly degenerate after they attach, taking no nourishment either from the female's blood or from the surrounding sea. They spawn once, then die and fall away, their mission accomplished. The diversity of behavior displayed by the ceratioid fishes helps us to understand how animal parasitism could have evolved from free-living, through intermediate, to fully dependent stages.

The Fish That Must Die for Its Young

The Pacific salmons invest heavily in eggs and take great risks in delivering them. The female chum salmon produces 3,000 to 4,000 eggs and travels as far as 2,000 miles inland to squirt them into the gravelly bed of some clear, bubbling stream. She may travel thirty miles in a day, then fight for every inch of progress through a rapid. A salmon has been known to leap a waterfall eleven feet high, bettering the record of an Olympic champion.[6]

A salmon traveling upstream does not feed. It grows steadily thinner as some of its tissues melt away in the effort of swimming and leaping and others change into roe or milt. Its digestive tract shrinks to make room for enlarging masses of sexual products and to lighten the body for travel.

As a boy I once caught a spawning chum with my hands and took it proudly home to mother. She baked it, but we couldn't eat it, for it had lost its texture and flavor. We fed it to the cat.

After the female spawns she lingers for a while at the nursery, her scales dulled, her fins ragged-edged, and her sides blotched with tufts of white fungus. At last she turns belly-up and drifts to the bank of the stream, there to be seized by a waiting bear, crow, eagle, or raven. If she spawned in autumn her eggs will hatch in the spring, and soon thereafter her fingerlings will go down to the sea.

During the oceanic stage of its life cycle the chum mingles freely with populations of other chums and of other salmon species. Come spawning time, each population sorts itself out and heads for home, guided by minute traces of plant and mineral oils that originated in the home stream. Each fish identifies them by smell (or taste), remembers them, and responds automatically to their lure.

Frogs That Give Birth Through the Mouth

Doris Cochran, of the United States National Museum, tells of the strange incubating-habits of an inch-long South American frog, discovered by Darwin in the nineteenth century.

Several males gather near a clutch of twenty to thirty eggs deposited by a single female. They stay on guard there for ten to twenty days, until the eggs are almost at the hatching point and the embryos are moving inside them. Each of the waiting males then picks up several eggs at a time with his tongue and slides them through the opening at the side of the tongue into the vocal pouch.[7]

Here in the dark of the male's throat they change from tadpoles to froglets. The father—real or foster—seems not to mind the pressure of five to fifteen babies against his body wall. They crawl in due time from his mouth and take up independent lives.

Even more incredible is the incubating pattern of the Australian stomach-brooding frog. The female swallows her fertilized eggs and

Stomach-brooding frog

lets them develop into tadpoles in the juices of her stomach. She stops feeding, of course. Her stomach becomes essentially a womb. At "near term" the froglets occupy so much room that they collapse the mother's lungs, forcing her to breathe through her moist skin.

Two men who studied live specimens in an aquarium reported that when one baby stirred it triggered a commotion lasting several minutes among the others.[8] By patiently holding an expectant mother in front of a serial-picture camera, the men were able to photograph her projectile vomiting of six babies, one by one, to distances as great as six feet! However, a mother who was not being forcibly held gave birth more leisurely. One of her babies sat reflectively on her lip for a while before hopping off; another retreated to her stomach. In a week's time the mother gave birth to twenty-six froglets equivalent in weight to 40 percent of her own antepartum weight and 66 percent of her postpartum weight.

The Australian frog's habit of incubating eggs within its stomach is unique in the animal kingdom. The habit may be a holdover from a misty past, when amphibians (which are descended from fishes) were trying to gain a foothold on the continents. If, at that time, nursery pools for tadpoles were scarce, the early amphibians would have found advantage in relying on self-contained, portable nurseries.

The Worst Journey in the World

In the annals of polar exploration one can read the account of a frightful trip made by Apsley Cherry-Garrard and two companions during the Antarctic winter of 1911. They were hoping to achieve a first for science—to collect eggs of the emperor penguin. They supposed that the flightless, cold-adapted emperor is a "living archetype" whose embryonic anatomy reflects the history of all avian evolution. The embryo, wrote Cherry-Garrard in his book, *The Worst Journey in the World*, "may prove the missing link between birds and the reptiles from which birds have sprung."[9]

Trudging over ice in continuous darkness for nineteen days, facing gales of wind and temperatures down to seventy-seven degrees below zero, the men hauled two sledges to the penguin rookery at Cape Crozier, arriving on July 20. There they stood in the bitter air, "three crystallized ragamuffins above the Emperor's home."[10]

They were the first humans to visit an emperor rookery during the egg-laying season. Through bloodshot eyes they saw that several of the birds were actually trying to incubate round lumps of dirty ice instead of eggs! (During incubation, the egg rests on top of the parent's feet, protected by a pouchlike fold of skin and feathers.) Although nearly exhausted, the men managed to collect three eggs, preserve them in alcohol, and carry them back to base camp.

Two years later Cherry-Garrard delivered them proudly to the Natural History Museum in London where, in due time, they were examined by experts. Alas! The embryos proved to be quite ordinary, although they did support a long held theory that feathers evolved from reptilian scales.

The broader theory, that every bird remembers its ancestral history and recounts it in a stuttering voice during its embryonic growth, is no longer questioned. Biologists recently gave it new sup-

Emperor penguin on egg

port; they produced chicken teeth![11] Considering that birds lost their functional teeth about a million centuries ago, this was no small feat. The biologists surgically removed four tooth buds from an embryonic mouse and replaced them with living tissues from the jaw of a chick. After several weeks the mouse had grown four strange teeth—more peglike and smoother crowned than normal mouse teeth. As fancifully stated by Terry Dunkle, the researchers "had shown that animals' cells may contain blueprints for obsolete body parts and that these cells may be coaxed into building them."[12]

Prehistoric hunters, familiar with the viscera of the animals they slaughtered, may have wondered why an embryo is so unlike the adult it is destined to become. It is not a miniature of the adult but a changeful little body that seems almost to lead a life of its own.

Biologists in the early part of the nineteenth century saw a parallel between the stages of embryonic growth and the "stages of nature" (lower to higher) that they perceived in the animal kingdom. They noted that an early human embryo has certain fishlike features, including paired gill pouches, and that an older embryo has features shared by all mammals (a tail, for example), and that a still older one has features uniquely human. Primitive, general characters appear before modern, special ones.

After Darwin's *Origin of Species* was published in 1859, biologists began to look more sharply at the relationship between the development of embryos and the development of animal diversity. "Embryology rises greatly in interest," wrote Darwin, "when we . . . look at the embryo as a picture, more or less obscured, of the common parent-form of each great class of animals."[13] In 1883, German zoologist Ernst Haeckel coined the phrase "ontogeny recapitulates phylogeny," or the history of the individual repeats the history of its kind.[14] This concept has been termed the theory of recapitulation.

But it is false. It fails, in the first place, to take into consideration the genetics of embryonic growth. The initial cleavage, or division, of a fertilized egg is followed by countless others, each directed by genes relayed from the egg. The cells resulting from the first few divisions are similar, while the cells appearing afterward are unlike. The newer cells are beginning to differentiate, grouping themselves into clusters which will become the separate tissues, organs, and parts of the body.

Should we be surprised, then, that a human embryo announces, early in its development, that it carries a few holdover genes identical with those that directed the development of an embryonic fish? That it carries an even larger load of the genes that directed the development of an embryonic Eocene mammal? As Simpson and Beck put it:

What is passed on from one generation to the next is a developmental mechanism. . . . The mechanism that produced a fish in our ancestors of about 300 million years ago has been inherited by us. In the meantime, however, it has undergone many and profound evolutionary changes and it produces quite a different kind of adult organism. The changes are more evident in later than in earlier developmental stages, and that is why an early human embryo is still rather like a correspondingly early fish embryo.[15]

The theory of recapitulation fails, in the second place, to take into consideration that most juvenile animals lead independent lives, and that natural selection works upon *them* as well as upon the adults they will become. The few species, including our own, that nourish dependent embryos comprise less than 1 percent of all animal species. The other 99-plus percent produce larvae, grubs, caterpillars, nits, nymphs (or juveniles by other names) that lead independent lives. There is no evidence that the free-swimming trochophore larva of a marine worm or a starfish represents its ancestral adult. What it represents is successful adaptation for life in the plankton, just as its parents represent adaptation for life on the bottom of the sea.

The Loneliest of Birds

In southwestern Australia there lives a bird that is perhaps the loneliest and most asocial of birds.[16] It hatches in isolation. Thereafter it neither seeks the company of its younger broodmates nor recognizes its own parents. Having little reason to communicate with others of its kind, it remains nearly mute through life. As a nineteenth-century ornithologist wrote, "its actions are suggestive of melancholy, for it . . . stalks along in a solemn manner as if the dreary nature of its surroundings and its solitary life weighed heavily on its spirits."[17]

It is the mallee fowl, a chicken-sized bird that lives in mallee (eucalyptus) scrublands. The hen lays her eggs in an incubator mound of earth mixed with fermenting vegetation—a genuine compost heap. A typical mound is fifteen feet across and three feet high, built with compost at its base, an egg chamber in its center, and a cap of sand on top. The hen leisurely lays one large egg every four to six days. Before laying, though, she waits for the cock to expose the egg chamber by raking off the sand with his large, strong feet.

Remarkably, the cock stands thermostat watch near the mound, visiting it frequently to test its temperature with his beak and to kick sand on or off to maintain the egg temperature near ninety-two degrees. At about the time in late spring when the compost is beginning to lose its heat of fermentation, the sun is rising high enough to warm the mound. But the cock can't control the heat precisely, with the result that a clutch of eggs may take anywhere from forty-nine to ninety days to hatch.

Mallee fowl chick

One by one the hatched and fully feathered chicks push and claw their way up through several feet of sand to the light of day. They rest awhile on top of the mound, then wander off. Within twenty-four hours they can fly. At the end of the six-month laying season the hen will have produced about twenty chicks. These siblings of the season, or broodmates, will range in age from a few days to several months.

Now comes an account of a dirty trick. Harold Frith, who studied the mallee fowl in all seasons of the year, declared that no one, least of all himself, had ever dreamed that a bird could control the temperature of a heap of sand and leaves so accurately in a region exposed to drought and cloudburst, and in air temperatures ranging from freezing to over one hundred degrees. So, in a mound where a cock had started to build a compost layer, Frith secretly hid an electric heating pad, remotely controlled. By turning the heat up or down during the next few months he nearly drove the cock crazy, but he did prove that "the thermometer bird" can hold the temperature of the egg chamber at ninety to ninety-five degrees, regardless of weather, by adjusting the thickness of the sand cap.

Then Frith built a hemispherical section of a mound in his workshop. Deep within it he placed several eggs about to hatch. Then, seated in a dark room and looking through a window, he saw the chicks break from their shells and climb to the surface. Even though buried alive for from two to fifteen hours after hatching, all made it. After struggling for a few minutes the typical chick would rest for an hour, breathing what little air filtered down to it through the sand grains, showing no signs of life other than the pulsing of its breast against the window.

Because we warm-blooded creatures prefer our warm-blooded kin in the wild to show at least a little parental interest in their children, we look askance at the mallee fowl. But 98 percent of all animal species are cold-blooded—in spirit as well as in body—and most of them don't recognize their own offspring. Indeed, if pushed, they will gobble them down as food. We should not judge wild animals by our own standards but admire them for their coordination and fitness, for the qualities that we as a species are in danger of losing.

Virgin Birth

Many lower animals still reproduce in the primal fashion by dividing or budding, while others, higher as well as lower on the Tree of Life, give birth generation after generation to fatherless young. Although the production of young from unfertilized eggs may seem a primitive trait, it is quite certainly a recent innovation—one that diverged from sexual reproduction.

The honeybee is one of many insects, some of whose young may develop from unfertilized eggs. When the queen bee mates with the male (drone) she stores his sperm in a special chamber. At the point of producing eggs she either does, or does not, fertilize them. Fertilized eggs become females (queens or workers), while unfertilized eggs become males.

About fifty years ago, biologists first learned that virgin birth is also possible in higher animals—at least in the laboratory. Gregory Pincus transferred an unfertilized rabbit's egg from one virgin female to a second who was pseudopregnant.[18] (She had been brought to this condition by an injection of luteinizing hormone.) In due time the second female produced an offspring which was normal in appearance but lacked paternal genes. The experiment was not easy; Pincus planted more than six hundred eggs in the genital tracts of nineteen rabbits before he was rewarded with two full-term offspring—one born dead and the other alive.

Nowadays, though, the public is overwhelmed by accounts of test-tube babies, man-mouse hybrids, spliced genes, zoo animals born from surrogate mothers, and similar biological *tours de force*.

Poultry scientists have long known that an egg from an unmated hen turkey will occasionally give rise to a young bird, or poult. More surprising, an egg from a *mated* hen will occasionally give rise to a poult bearing no resemblance to the father. In both cases, the poult develops parthenogenetically. Department of Agriculture scientists have found that a white hen mated with a buff gobbler may produce one or more white poults, containing maternal chromosomes only, in a hatch of mainly buff ones, containing chromosomes from both parents.

But how can a mated hen produce "fatherless" poults? Evidently because copulation is not always followed by fertilization. In the turkey, as in other birds, the developing egg, or ovum, normally ejects one of its two sets of chromosomes before it leaves the ovary and starts down the egg tube. This routine ejection keeps the number of chromosomes from doubling with each new generation. Parthenogenesis is evidently caused by failure of an ovum to reject one of its chromosome sets. In consequence, although sperms may eventually reach this ovum, and swarm around it, they are blocked by the unejected set from reaching their destination in the ovum's nucleus. Thus the paternal chromosomes are unable to combine with the maternal ones, and a fatherless embryo results.

Several years before the Pincus experiment with rabbits, Carl and Laura Hubbs had discovered what they called "apparent parthenogenesis" in a *wild* vertebrate, in a fish. If not virgin birth, it was very close. While Carl and Laura were netting Amazon mollies in Texas and nearby Mexico, they examined 2,000 captive specimens without finding a single male.[19] But later, when they raised specimens in an aquarium, they learned that a female would not give birth until she had mated with a male of a closely related species. Puzzled, Carl and Laura concluded that sperm somehow triggers the development of the eggs while itself taking no part in heredity. But if so, why had they found no males among the 2,000 fish they sampled in the wild? Do females reproduce spontaneously (in the absence of males) in wild environments but not in the laboratory? Their questions could not be answered at the time.

Now it is known that ten or more species of livebearers—mollies, guppies, topminnows, and relatives—and one species of silverside occur in nature only as females. Their remote ancestors were evidently hybrids between closely related, normal, bisexual species. Since unisexual reproduction is rare in higher animals—displayed by fewer than 0.1 percent of vertebrates—it may be an evolutionary blind alley. Or it may be a promising experiment. We should not underestimate the inventiveness of Nature.

To be sure, unisexual reproduction doubles the fecundity rate, for its practitioners need waste no time producing males. Theoretically, one unisexual aphid could generate a population of 300 million in the time taken by one pair of bisexuals to generate a population of only one thousand.[20] The catch is that unisexual species are especially vulnerable to sudden changes in their surroundings. Having adopted a unisexual style of life, they have lost the opportunity to acquire—except through rare mutations—new genes that might equip them to survive through environmental perturbations.

"Since no major group of animals or plants is completely parthenogenetic," concludes Roger Blackman, "it would appear that for some reason parthenogenesis cannot stand the test of time as an alternative strategy to sex."[21]

As though they understood this principle, rotifers, water fleas, cynipid gall wasps, and aphids will occasionally produce a generation containing males, then return to producing females only.

Sex Ambivalence

And there are certain animals that, while still young, can "choose" to become either male or female. There are certain other animals that are destined to remain hermaphroditic throughout life. I write of normal animals, not of freaks like the egg-laying "rooster" that results from an accident at the embryonic or juvenile stage. Early damage to a hen's ovarian tissue may stimulate her to produce the comb and the crowing voice of a rooster.

Sex in a small estuarine fish, the Atlantic silverside, is strongly influenced by the temperature of the water in which the larva develops. The female sheds her eggs among fronds of seaweed during two to three months in spring and early summer. For a while, when the sea is cold, about 70 percent of the developing larvae turn into females. Later, when the water grows warmer, the ratio drops to 40 percent females. Moreover, in the laboratory a day-old larva raised in cold water (52°–66°) is twice as likely to mature into a female as is one raised in warm water (63°–77°).[22]

The adaptive value of sex ambivalence in the silverside is evidently this: by investing heavily in females at the start of the breeding season the population is guaranteed that, whatever happens later, adequate numbers of the more important sex will be on hand.

Or, as silverside authority David Conover puts it, "Temperature is merely a physiological cue telling the individual whether it has been born early or late in the breeding season and, hence, whether it will experience a long or short growing season. Individuals born in colder thermal regimes generally become female because they will become [larger and fitter than males] by virtue of a longer growing season."[23] Maximum fecundity being the silverside's "goal," small females are penalized more than small males, for smallness in a female means fewer eggs, while smallness in a male is less important. Regardless of his size, within limits, he can provide sperm in quantity surplus to the needs of the population.

Sex ambivalence is rare among vertebrate animals, being known only in certain fishes, in one family of turtles, and in one species of alligator. It is not, however, uncommon among lower animals. For example, the larva of the marine echiurid worm, Bonellia, is sexually indifferent. If it happens to settle in a population where females are abundant it becomes a male, and *vice versa*. "Thus," writes evolutionist George Williams, "each individual adjusts its sex to the opportunities presented by its demographic environment."[24] This adjustment is spectacular, for if the larva becomes a female it develops into an ovoid body fully an inch long, but if it becomes a male it remains a speck barely visible to the unaided eye. The male wormlet takes up residence inside its mate's genital tract. The larval worm unwittingly contributes to the good of its population by postponing (so to speak) its choice of gender until it has assessed its surroundings. We can only marvel at the delicate balance among the drifting pheromones of adult Bonellia, which, as they are sensed and interpreted by a larva, can prompt its germ-cells to mature into either ovaries or testes.

I wish to make clear that it is first the *individual* silverside or echiurid worm, and second its *group*, that benefits from the ability to mature either as male or female. And of course the individual is wholly blind to its own importance within the group. It lives, and moves, and has its being "by the numbers." I shall have more to say about group selection in the chapter "Life in Populations."

The Meaning of Sex Ratios

A tabulation of sex ratios at birth or hatching for eighteen species of mammals and ten species of birds shows averages of: mammals, 51.4 percent males and 48.6 percent females; birds, 51.5 percent males and 48.5 percent females.[25] To explain this sexual imbalance in mammals, biologists theorize that, since the sperms which determine maleness carry a lighter genome than do those which determine femaleness, the lighter sperms swim faster toward the egg and are more likely to fertilize it. Perhaps so. This explanation will not hold for birds, however, where the sperms that determine maleness carry the *heavier* load. So far as I know, a good explanation of sex imbalance at birth or hatching has yet to be offered.

When biologists find that the sex ratio in a wild animal population has swung very far from 50:50, they wonder why. They ask, "What benefit can sex imbalance bring?" One answer is that hard times, with attendant stress, may lead to the production of the cheaper sex. Redwing blackbirds prove the point.[26] Male redwings are larger than females and are thus more costly to produce. When food in a redwing marsh declines, fewer males than females survive to the fledgling stage. The result is beneficial to the redwing's population and its species. If birds of only one sex can be favored in the race for survival during hard times, it had better be the females, for these can more quickly restore the population when the environment improves. A man and three women stranded on an island can, if all are willing, populate it sooner than two men and two women.

It is more difficult to explain why, in hard times, the sex ratio *even at birth* should have turned in favor of the females of a species. In such instances it is clear that the pregnant female's poor condition harms her male fetuses more than her female ones. But why? Sex-biased mortality at birth has been observed among deer, rabbits, dogs, sheep, and captive mink. These species would seem to possess uncanny genes which, as two biologists put it, "favor parental ability to adjust the sex ratio of offspring . . . according to parental ability to invest."[27]

Even more puzzling is the fact that the sex ratio at birth among seals may shift progressively in favor of females *during the pupping season*. British gray seals usually give birth from mid-October to late November. Their pupping season opens with a newborn ratio near male 60:female 40 and, having reversed itself, closes near 40:60. Among the Weddell seals of Antarctica the ratio opens near 56:44 and closes near 44:56. Among Antipodean fur seals it opens near 54:46 and closes near 41:59.[28]

But, again, why? These ratios vary under seemingly normal, not stressful, circumstances. You will perhaps guess that the males are born earlier because they need more time to reach adult size, when they will greatly outweigh the females. But adult male Weddell seals are *smaller* than adult females; your guess must be ruled out.

When the true explanation is discovered it will surely confirm the principle that whenever Nature manipulates a character as fundamental as a sex ratio, the result will somehow benefit the species.

McClure and Her Wood Rats

Polley Ann McClure, of Indiana University, had a hunch that certain animals can directly bias the sex ratio of their offspring "whenever they gain more in [racial] fitness by producing more of one sex than they lose by producing fewer of the other."[29] In hard times they may turn to sex-biased infanticide.

So she raised in captivity twenty-two wood rat litters, each with mother and pups. She nearly starved twelve of the litters and gave

Wood rats

the other ten—the controls—ample food. During a typical three-week nursing period the starved mothers favored their daughters, while the control mothers favored neither sex. The average starved mother's energy investment in female pups was 68 percent, but in male pups only 32 percent. "Discrimination against males," explained McClure, "took the form of active rejection by the mother."[30] In every starved litter except one, all the male pups died before any female did.

Two questions come to mind. Considering that a starved mother begins to reject her male pups only five days after birth, while they are still tiny and naked, how can she possibly recognize their sex? McClure suggests that male pups may excrete in their urine sex-specific hormones which the mother can identify by taste. The second question goes deeper. Why does Nature let the males and not the females suffer the higher mortality? McClure suggests that, since wood rats are polygynous (one male mating with several females), males are the more expendable.

The truly remarkable point about infanticide is that the mother acts as if she could foresee the *future* advantage of a population containing more females than males. If she were concerned only with culling the *present* population to fit its food supply she would reject males and females equally, without bias.

It is humbling to reflect that wood rats seem to control their populations with less effort than do we, the smarter species.

Hermaphroditism

Hermaphroditic breeding is the rule among many lower animals, including sponges, jellyfishes, worms, and molluscs. Slugs and earthworms (for example), although not self-fertilizing, are equipped with both ovaries and testes. Copulating individuals line up belly to belly, with their heads pointing in opposite directions, to mutually discharge sperms into the other's body (see p. 73).

Hermaphroditism is rare among higher animals. Among vertebrates it is evidently confined to a few fresh-water and marine fishes. One of these is the hagfish or slime eel, a creature horribly repulsive in habits as well as appearance. It resembles a short section of dirty broomhandle—rubbery, jawless, boneless, and nearly blind. It writhes its way into the mouth or anus of larger fishes and devours them from within, leaving only a bag of skin and bones.

Strangely, while the breeding cycle of the hagfish has been studied for nearly a century, it is still poorly known. All stages between hermaphrodites and males or females can be found. The most likely explanation of the cycle goes like this: individuals are hermaphroditic in early life, having both ovaries and testes. By the time they attain a body length of twelve to thirteen inches they are either functionally male, or functionally female, or neither (neuter and sterile). Perhaps, even, the same individual can at first be a male and later a female. No one is sure. The lowly hagfish, wrote Fridtjof Nansen, "seems still to be seeking, without yet reaching, that mode of reproduction which is most profitable for it in the struggle for existence."[31]

Hermaphroditism is only one of countless reproductive strategies—only one of countless pathways to perpetuation of the species. Biologists believe that it has selective advantages where populations are thinly scattered, where individuals have difficulty finding mates. Here an individual able to to function either as a male or a female will find that *any* chance-encountered stranger (of its own species) is "the right one."

Another advantage of hermaphroditism is presumed where the female of the species is larger than the male. Eggs, being larger than sperms, are the more costly to produce. Hence, if a larva capable of choosing its future gender happens to arrive in an especially favorable habitat—a Promised Land—it will better serve its species by growing large, turning female, and producing eggs. If, on the other hand, it arrives later in the same habitat, when all the best places have been taken, it can still serve by remaining small and producing sperm. (Cold comfort to male chauvinists.)

The Salamander That Breeds in Youth

So, unisexual reproduction is a strategy that quickens the reproductive rate of a species. Breeding while still in the larval stage is another. Paedogenesis (literally, "descent through children") is practiced by the aquatic tadpoles of a Mexican salamander.[32] Called locally an axolotl, each tadpole matures sexually, engages in courtship, and produces eggs or sperms before it reaches adulthood. However, an axolotl can be forced to metamorphose into a dry-land adult by treating it with thyroxin and by lowering the water level of its pond, thus making gill breathing more difficult and lung breathing easier.

When the axolotl was discovered it was thought to represent a new, strictly aquatic, gill-breathing race. Later it was found capable of maturing into a land dwelling tiger salamander very like those that breed over much of North America. Thus an "axolotl" is simply an aberrant tiger salamander which, constrained by the poverty of its habitat, begins to reproduce as soon as it can, even before it has reached its potential adult size.

Adaptation brought success to the axolotl. Its ancestors lived in clear mountain pools deficient in the iodine necessary for normal thyroid secretion and normal body growth. "Retarded" through life, those ancestral forms nonetheless learned genetically to breed.

Life in Populations

A SPECIES IS MORE THAN A BIOLOGICAL CATEGORY; it is a real population, living or extinct. Thus the origin of species is also the origin of populations. The present chapter illustrates some of the ways by which animals regulate their own population levels. These include aggressive behavior and active sex discrimination. Singly and collectively they affect the evolution of the species.

Often at my suburban home I must trap a wood mouse that has found its way into the pantry. A sad duty. I caught one yesterday, and as I weighed the soft little body in my hand, I saw that both its ears were scarred as if they had been torn or bitten. And so they had, for adult mice, impelled to drive juveniles from the nest, attack them roughly. This is one of Nature's ways of insuring that no mouse population will outgrow the carrying capacity, or food and shelter resources, of its habitat. The driving out of juveniles is, of course, a "selfish" act, the consequences of which benefit the group.

For every newborn mouse, then, its family becomes part of its environment, and overcrowding in the family can become an environmental threat as dangerous as harsh weather, flooding, or forest fire. A mouse in a population growing rapidly must compete ever more desperately for food. It loses weight and its fertility drops. Hunger drives it from shelter in search of food, thereby increasing its exposure to attack by weasel, fox, or owl. And disease flares up because a weakened mouse is less resistant than a strong one and because contagions tend to spread rapidly in crowds.

These population facts of life came to mind yesterday as I contemplated a pair of small gray ears, torn as though scarred or bitten.

Gopher mounds

The Rewards of Hostility

Pocket gophers—ratlike animals that burrow in prairie soils of the American West—are strongly asocial. Driven by instinct to maintain a personal distance which is partly geographical and partly psychological, they stake out individual claims on the land. On many treeless prairies of the American West from Canada to Mexico they build spectacular nesting mounds of earth, commonly spaced eight

Wood mouse

to ten per acre, some rising higher than a man's head. Their spacing is a mark of animal territoriality and is a striking example of the social use of space.[1]

Gophers work desperately for a living, tunneling through the soil in all seasons of the year in search of the plant roots and stems upon which they feed. Their incisor teeth grow continuously, for if they did not, they would soon be worn to the gumline by the abrasion of gritty foods. Biologist Tom Kennerly weighed all the soil moved by one gopher in one year: it amounted to a whopping 2.6 tons.[2] And he weighed only the tailings left in small heaps on the surface, not those disposed of in abandoned tunnels.

Two other biologists who studied gopher behavior in Colorado verified the solitary nature of the species.[3] Of 492 gophers that were caught in traps, only *four* were associated with companions in the same tunnel system. The gopher's hostile behavior, insofar as it prevents overuse of a limited food resource, is advantageous to the species. It confers survival value.

So, one might say that hostile behavior by wood mice and gophers is their way of controlling their own populations. True enough, if we can agree that no mouse or gopher has the faintest notion of *why* it is impelled to disperse its relatives and if we can agree that internal, or within-species, regulation is only one of many natural population controls.

Darwin made a similar point in *The Origin of Species*. Discussing "mutual checks to increase," he told how insects regulate the number of cattle in Paraguay.[4] There inhabit that country, he explained, certain botflies that lay their eggs on the raw navels of newborn calves and cause fatal infections. Insectivorous birds keep the flies in check. As the birds increase in numbers, the flies decrease . . . causing the cattle to increase and to browse the vegetation more heavily . . . reducing the habitat for birds . . . depressing the bird population . . . allowing the flies to rebuild their numbers . . . causing the cattle to decrease. "And so," wrote Darwin, "onwards in ever-increasing circles of complexity." Although he did not actually see this circular drama played, he knew the actors and knew their repertoires.

Let me repeat a fable told by a zoology professor long ago. I recall it as part Darwin and part Professor Kincaid. No matter; it offers insight into population dynamics.

Given that bumblebees build nests, and that many of the nests are destroyed by field mice. *Given* that bumblebees are important pollinators of red clover. *Given* that roving cats kill mice, and that cats flourish in the company of maiden ladies. *Then*, if the bees increase, the clover crop will increase, bringing wealth to the village and enabling bachelors to marry maidens. Out will go the cats, the mice will increase, and the bee population will decline.

A fable? Yes, although matched in real life by natural population controls of such complexity that biologists despair of comprehending them.

Calhoun and His White Mice

John Calhoun, at the National Institute of Mental Health, has devoted an illustrious career to understanding the sociology of rodent populations as a step toward understanding their biology and, in the end, their population ups and downs. In one experiment he released four pairs of mice in a small Utopia—a room about eight feet square provided with ample food, water, and nesting material.[5] The mice began enthusiastically to breed, with the following results:

At Day 560 from the start of the experiment the population peaked at 2,200 mice, then began to decline. All "founding mothers" still alive had entered menopause.

By Day 681 many mice were huddling together, psychologically withdrawn. They fought sporadically.

By Day 920 all mating was presumed to have ceased.

By Day 1,588 the population had fallen to 27 adult mice, none younger than 2.7 years. Hoping to rejuvenate the colony, Calhoun introduced 8 new males, but by now the social order was in ruins. No young mice resulted.

And at Day 1,644, after 4.5 years, the last mouse died.

Calhoun explained that during the declining, or crowded, phase of the cycle, young mice were prematurely rejected by their mothers. They were thrown into a crowd where their every attempt to practice instinctive social behavior was interrupted. Young females never learned to be females. Young males never learned to be males, but instead turned into creatures that Calhoun named "the beautiful ones," who spent their time eating, drinking, sleeping, or grooming. Both sexes became "autistic-like creatures capable only of the most simple behaviors compatible with physiological survival."[6]

In his study of crowding, Calhoun looked also at the spatial distribution of wild, free-living mammals such as mice, shrews, and gophers, that typically defend individual territories. Ideally, each territory would be six-sided, for the hexagon is the ideal unit in a tightly packed, two-dimensional configuration. (Witness the honeycomb cell.) Noting that an animal living in a field of hexagonal territories has six nearest and eighteen next-nearest neighbors (total twenty-four), Calhoun suggested that the magic number *six* has left its imprint on man's society. Man may have originated "out of an evolutionary line in which optimum adjustment demanded living in small groups not exceeding twice twelve individuals."[7]

This is a captivating thought for teachers, preachers, social workers, and others who deal in interpersonal relationships. On the other hand, it may be nonsense. The evolution of hominid societies came about through the gradual *abandonment* of individual territories, hexagonal or otherwise. Even if remote hominid ancestors did defend territories, as do mice, shrews, and gophers, we need only to compare modern mice, shrews and gophers with modern hominids to appreciate the vast difference between the life styles of the two groups. I'm told by an anthropologist that, while pre-agricultural humans commonly lived in bands of twenty-five to fifty, there are plausible explanations for that tendency, most of them based on foraging and food-sharing strategies and on division of labor between the sexes. To believe that hexagonal territoriality left traces in modern hominid societies, this authority says, is to believe in the existence of a phylogenetic inertia for which there is no evidence.

The Meaning of Clutch-Size

Two species of birds that visit my home in summer are roughly similar in body size and in feeding habits but very unlike in the number of eggs they lay. The band-tailed pigeon lays one or two eggs, while the California quail lays ten to fifteen or more. Why the great difference?

The answer is simply that the distant ancestors of the two birds took separate reproductive paths that progressively diverged. The pigeon now builds a sheltered nest and lays an egg that hatches soon into a naked and helpless squab which will be fed for several days by its mother. But the quail builds its nest on the open ground and lays numerous eggs that hatch slowly into precocious, fully-feathered and active chicks. Termed "nest-fleers," the chicks jump from the nest to search for insects on the very day they hatch. (Their diet will later include seeds and other plant foods.)

The point is that the average setting or clutch of every bird contains the number of eggs that will guarantee the survival of the most young to maturity. If a female lays too few eggs, her bloodline will disappear, swamped in time by the lines of other birds that lay more. If she lays too many, most of her young will perish from undernourishment, with the same unfortunate effect on the bloodline.

Quail nest with eggs

Thus Nature works continuously to maintain a clutch-size which, for a given species, varies within narrow limits only.

What Nature is engaged in here is stabilizing selection, a process that promotes the average individuals in a population at the expense of the extremes. It takes place in all species, including the human, where it is expressed (for example) as average size at birth. Babies weighing about eight pounds are more likely to survive than are heavier or lighter ones.

The adaptive meaning of clutch-size was illuminated forty years ago by David Lack, of Oxford University. He showed that the survival of Swiss starlings does indeed vary with clutch-size.[8] He banded nestling birds in more than four thousand nests, recording at the same time the number of birds per nest (which number was, for his purpose, equivalent to clutch-size). Three months later he captured as many fledgling birds as he could. He learned that clutch-size varied from one to ten, *five* being the most common, and that fledglings raised from broods of *five* made up the highest percentage of all banded birds recaptured. So he concluded that "the commonest brood-size found in nature is also the size with optimum productivity."[9]

In perfecting the ideal clutch, Nature gradually identifies what market specialists call the sensitive point—that point away from which, in either direction, the seller of a product finds his profits falling off. If he has set its price too low, sales will be brisk but earnings marginal; if he has set its price too high, profit per item will be high but total sales disappointing.

Cyclic Populations

Plagues, or irruptions, of mice were mentioned by Aristotle in the fourth century B.C. and later by Old Testament writers. Now it is known that they tend to occur at intervals of three to four years. I was once camped in an aspen grove in the Colorado Rockies during an irruption of field mice. As night fell, the sound of their tiny bodies moving through the dry grass was one long, continuous whisper.

Wildlife populations, such as those of field mice and lemmings, that fluctuate strongly and cyclically are partly self-regulating, for their increase is limited by critical changes in *the quality of the population itself.* After biologists began to study the cyclic behavior of mice and lemmings it took them thirty years to realize that environmental determinants—such as weather, food, predation, and disease—contribute less to cyclic responses than do factors inherent in the mice. These factors are genetic, and they take effect through social behavior.

Charles Elton and Dennis Chitty, of Oxford University, and Judith Myers and Charles Krebs, of the University of British Columbia, are a few of the many researchers whose names are linked with the exploration of population cycles. At first their interest focused on the dramatic "bust" that typically follows a population "boom." Where a hundred mice may have flourished in autumn, only a dozen may be alive by the end of winter. The researchers asked, What conceivable agent can reverse the growth of a population seemingly in good health and surrounded by food? This question led to examination of the whole machinery of population control among rodents.

And it raised questions for which answers are still being sought. So biologists live-trap mice, mark them, release them, and retrap them. To estimate the influence of male aggression on the fertility of laboratory populations, they castrate some of the males. They imprison mice in outdoor pens and study changes in body condition and behavior as the population increases. (One population of mice rose to 24,000 per acre! I wish I could have seen that squeaking universe.)[10] They measure the impact of mice on the food resource, as a rancher measures the impact of cattle on his pastures.

When I once visited Chitty at his laboratory in England he was weighing the tiny adrenal and thymus glands of field mice, trying to measure indirectly the importance of stress as a regulator of population growth. He was exploring the idea that hormone feedback, in response to increased social pressure, can limit population growth.

Students of cyclic populations now widely agree that social interaction is the compelling force that finally pushes these populations downhill. Social interaction leads to strife, and strife leads either to mass emigration or to reproductive failure, that is, to failure of conception, to resorption of embryos, or to abortion. So, most populations decline from low productivity rather than from high mortality, as earlier supposed.

Population students do not agree, however, on the importance of *dimorphism* in regulating population cycles. Dimorphism is the occurrence of two genetically distinct forms of the same species in the same place. In the Calhoun camp are those who believe that hormone feedback alone can stimulate emigration and suppress reproduction. In the Chitty camp are those who believe that two distinct forms of animals—the Aggressives and the Dociles—are always present in a given population, though in proportions that vary with population density. The two forms look alike but behave differently.

The Chitty hypothesis was framed by its author in 1971:

All species of animals have a form of behavior that can prevent unlimited increase in population density.[11]

It may be, says Charles Krebs, "one of the last grand generalizations of population ecology."[12]

If the Chitty hypothesis is true, field mice limit their populations about like this: as a population grows, the Aggressives deny living space to the Dociles and inhibit their reproduction. But—and this is important—the Aggressives are genetically more irritable and less fertile than the Dociles. So reproduction almost stops, with the result that the population crashes. Slowly the surviving Dociles, now unbothered by Aggressives, rebuild it.

The Chitty hypothesis offers a plausible answer to the long-debated question, Why do field mice recover so slowly after a crash? Chitty replies that since food shortage, disease, and predation have been ruled out by experiment as critical limiting factors, the population must therefore be limited by its own poor fertility. A second argument in favor of his hypothesis is inferential. Since Nature "rewards" countless dimorphic species, why not field mice as well?

Dimorphism is fascinating. It seems to be one of the more useful genetic tricks that enable animals to survive through changing environments, including changing population densities.

I don't wish to leave the impression that the Chitty hypothesis explains mammalian cycles to everyone's satisfaction, for questions continue to trouble. Why, for example, are not all species of small mammals cyclic? And why are not all populations of a given species cyclic throughout the entire range of that species?

Group Selection

The driving motor in evolution is selective elimination of unfit (genetically less efficient) individuals. But individuals live in groups of various kinds—groups that range from the tightly knit societies of termites to the rarified populations of South American condors. The behavior of an individual by itself is seldom like its behavior within the species group. This fact has led to study of group selection, a process defined by Douglas Futuyma as "the differential rate of origination or extinction of whole populations . . . on the basis of differences among them in one or more characteristics."[13]

Let me offer an example of group behavior. In 1937 the International Whaling Commission banned the hunting of right whales, a species that had been brought to the verge of extinction by commercial whaling. But the whale population did not later recover; today it is estimated at only 2,000 to 4,000, worldwide. If, let us say, there had been 2,000 whales in 1937, and if their numbers had grown under protection at a reasonable 5 percent per year, there would now be nearly 20,000. One explanation for the failure of the population to bounce back is that by 1937 other plankton-feeding whales, such as the sei and fin, had moved into the right whales' econiche and were taking foods formerly consumed by them. Perhaps so, but why, then, after the right whales were protected, did they not repossess their former niche?

Abusive whaling caused an enduring and perhaps irreversible change in a group. It effected a change in the genetic composition—an evolutionary change—in that group. One cannot say with assurance that competition for food was responsible, for there may have been other factors, especially those subtle sociobiological ones that exert greatest influence upon low populations.

The effects of group selection are best measured in insular populations such as those of mice living on small islands, of plankton crustaceans in small lakes, of flightless beetles on mountain tops, and of insects in laboratory cultures. Biologist Philip Darlington observed on Mount Washington, New Hampshire, that a flightless form of ground beetle is virtually the only form present.[14] When a *flying* form reaches the mountain top, as it occasionally does, it or its immediate descendants soon disappear as a result either of being outclassed by the established, better adapted flightless residents or of being genetically swamped by hybridization with them.

Michael Wade, at the University of Chicago, carried out a laboratory experiment showing, he concluded, that "group selection can accomplish a genetic change which occurs rapidly and is in large magnitude."[15] He raised flour beetles in jars on a diet of wheat flour and yeast. He started with sixteen adults per population, or culture, and planned to examine the population at the end of each generation (which for flour beetles is about thirty-three days). During each examination he would count the number of adults per jar in relation to the number of immatures. A high count would mean that the culture was in "good health." (I simplify here. Wade already knew from previous studies that the time to natural extinction of a culture can be predicted early in its history from the percentage of adults within it.) After each examination he would separate those cultures having *higher* ratios of adults to immatures from those having *lower*, and would repeat the separation after each subsequent generation. His plan was not unlike that of an animal breeder developing two strains of white mice, in one of which the females consistently give birth to four litters per year, the other to six.

Wade charted the course of his beetle populations through eight generations, while the spread between the artificially selected high breeders and low breeders progressively widened. In the ninth generation, the average number of adults in comparable populations was 178 for high breeders and 20 for low breeders.

The experiment had not been designed to reveal the individual factors in the natural selective process. It showed nothing, for example, about the importance of cannibalism within the cultures. What it did show was how an entire *group* responded to changes in its environment. The group announced the state of its health at various population levels. No researcher could have predicted those states, partly because no researcher could have measured the strength of the many separate forces, pro and con life, to which an individual beetle is exposed, either alone or in the group.

Although biologists no longer doubt that Darwinian evolution explains the growth of animal diversity through time, they continue to study the dynamics of evolution. Accepting the *what* of evolution, they persist in asking *how*? They try to measure the forces that change its motion and direction. They search for intermediates between parasitic and free-living flies—for the missing links that might reveal how parasitic behavior evolved. They search for meaning in the strange sexual behavior of the anglerfishes. "Why," they wonder, "is sexuality in the animal world so incredibly diverse?" They try to understand the complexities of group foraging, food partitioning, and predator avoidance. Thus, evolution is continually taking place, not only in organisms but in evolutionary thought.

Tempo and Mode
in Evolution

T HE TITLE OF THIS CHAPTER is that of George Gaylord Simpson's book, published forty years ago.[1] Its thesis was "that the history of life . . . is consistent with the evolutionary processes of genetic mutation and variation, guided toward adaptation of populations by natural selection." How precisely put!

Evolution means change in the genetic makeup of populations.It means speciation. Unmistakable clues to change are hidden in the comparative anatomy, genetics, embryology, and molecular chemistry of animals. Clues are also hidden in the distribution of animals—in their zoogeography. The most convincing evidence of evolutionary change is the great Tree of Life itself. (Or the Bramble of Life, for it is a sprawling body from which untold numbers of twigs were falling away while others were sprouting.) Planet Earth has nurtured billions of species. At least 99.9 percent are now extinct, and at least 90 percent left no descendants. The great dinosaurs, for example, left no descendants, while some of the smaller ones gave rise to modern birds. And from the beginning of the Cambrian Period, 570 million years ago, the diversity of marine fossil families has increased about twenty-five-fold.[2]

The Rate of Speciation

When a population finds opportunity to expand—to pioneer a new site—it may change rapidly. When Polynesians first brought the banana to the Hawaiian Islands about a thousand years ago they also brought stowaways, pyraustid moths that feed only on bananas. Now there are five endemic species of pyraustids on the islands. Because they do not resemble relatives living outside the islands but *do* resemble each other, they evidently radiated from one founder stock—the stowaways—in only a thousand years.[3]

English sparrows were introduced into eastern North America around 1850. During the following century they spread rapidly from the Atlantic to the Pacific and from Canada to Central America. In the meanwhile they changed in color, pattern, size, and shape—each population changing in ways that enabled it to fit better within the habitat where it settled. Northern birds grew larger in body—an adaptation to cold—while Northwest Coast birds became darker in plumage than those of the arid Southwest—adaptations, respectively, to darker and lighter soils.[4] As the various flocks became geographically and reproductively isolated, those individuals in each flock that, by genetic chance, fit better into the local environment contributed a greater proportion of *their* genes to each new generation.

As shown by this example, the hammer of evolution, given the raw material with which to work (the genetic diversity of the pioneer birds) and given a hundred sparrow generations, forged at least three varieties now fully equivalent to zoological races. Evolution can at times move astonishingly fast.

Man, working with captive animals, can create new varieties and even new species in fewer than a hundred generations, although he must employ the same machinery of selection that creates species in the wild. It is a machinery which, through his ability to predict and to make value judgments, he has learned to control for his own ends.

Artificial breeding sometimes involves the creation of hybrids such as mules, having horse and ass parentage, and cattalos, having cattle and American buffalo parentage. Annie Gray, British geneticist, has published a list of 573 hybrids reported from the Mammalia alone.[5] Some were born in captivity and others in the wild. When hybridization takes place in the wild it rarely initiates a new bloodline, for hybrid offspring are usually sterile.

Shell of land snail

Two biologists studying Darwin's ground finch on one of the Galapagos Islands from 1975 to 1978 were afforded a rare insight into the dynamics of speciation.[6] By 1977 they had collected a good deal of information on the bird's biology and on the abundance of various seeds that compose its diet. Following a severe drought in 1977 the finches did not breed at all; their numbers dropped to 15 percent of normal. Significantly, the birds that did survive into 1978 were the larger ones, especially males having large beaks capable of cracking the harder seeds that also survived the drought. The finch population, concluded the biologists, had passed "through a bot-

Darwin's ground finch

tleneck of intensive selection pressure," fortunately when observers were there to document the passage.

We may assume that many genes for smallness of body were lost to the population through the death of small birds. But similar genes would have survived, hidden within the bodies of larger birds, awaiting the favorable day when genes for smallness would become the fitter kind—those more capable of extending their own ratio in the population. The point is, again, that natural selection, by working on individuals, works ultimately on populations and species.

It would be of some interest to know whether speciation through time has taken place gradually or by leaps. Gradually, thought Darwin, quoting that old canon of natural history, *"Natura non facit saltum."*[7] He ascribed the apparent saltations or leaps in the fossil record to the incompleteness of the record—to scanty knowledge of the missing links that must have existed in the intervals between leaps. The fossil record, he wrote, is "a history of the world imperfectly kept, and written in a changing dialect; of this history we possess the last volume alone. . . . Of this volume, only here and there a short chapter has been preserved; and of each page, only here and there a few lines."[8] But opinion seems to be moving away from Darwin's idea that evolution is gradual and toward the idea that it is episodic—often interrupted by genetic "revolutions" that give rise to new species.

A recent dramatic find in Kenya supports the latter idea, namely, that evolution is best represented by the model called punctuated equilibrium. Evolutionist Peter Williamson collected the fossil remains of 3,300 freshwater molluscs from a sedimentary bed about one-quarter mile thick. This bed shows no evidence of having been disturbed since it was laid down; it has been called an uncensored page of fossil history. Williamson patiently traced the evolution of thirteen lineages of shells. His findings provide, in his words, "the first fine-scaled paleontological resolution of events during speciation."[9]

He learned through computer analysis of the shells that a typical species persisted, little changed, for 3 to 5 million years, when it abruptly began to change. Each transformation coincided with a drop in lake level, an event that doubtless created environmental stress. Within 5,000 to 50,000 years (say, 20,000 snail generations), a typical species passed through intermediate stages and emerged as a distinctly new one. Because the thirteen lineages represent snails and clams widely diverse in size and habits, the importance of Williamson's research is greater than had he been able to trace the lineage of one species alone.

Evolutionist David Raup is likewise interested in the viability, or geological life, of the average species.[10] He recently cast his analytical net over the fossil remains of about 8,500 genera and subgenera of invertebrates that lived at one time or another during the 570 million years of the Cambrian-through-Recent periods. When he computed the survivorship pattern for each lineage he found that the patterns were surprisingly regular, and that the average species survived for 11.1 million years.

His estimate is higher than Williamson's 3 to 5 million years. The difference can be laid, I think, to the likelihood that small snails and clams (Williamson's material) living in a freshwater lake changed more rapidly than did invertebrates living in the ocean (Raup's material), for the ocean is a more stable environment than is any lake.

The so-called relict fauna of one of the world's most ancient lakes illuminates this point. Lake Tanganyika, in East Africa, is a huge freshwater body more than 1,400 feet deep, dating from Miocene time. There still live in its waters marine-like snails, crabs, prawns, and jellyfishes. Lingering shadows of the past, they are the descendants of organisms that inhabited the lake when it was a briny extension of the ocean about 10 million years ago. When earth movements landlocked the extension its waters slowly turned fresh. Some of the original forms, such as starfishes and lamp shells, could not tolerate the change; they perished. Others could and did adapt to fresh water.

One of my friends, who lives in rural England, swears that hedgehogs have "learned genetically" within our century to run from an approaching automobile instead of curling up in the defensive posture of their pre-auto ancestors. Certain oddball individuals in the primary stock who elected to run were evidently those who survived to breed. They and their offspring steadily advanced the numerical importance within the hedgehog population of their own innovative (or lucky) kind.

Recent studies in geology and astronomy are providing tentative answers to a question first raised more than a century ago: "Why, as shown by the fossil record, do the faunas of the world change abruptly and profoundly at certain times?" Major revolutions took place at the beginning and end of the Cambrian, and at the ends of the Devonian, Permian, Triassic, and Cretaceous periods. Approaching the dawn of the Cambrian, life was still essentially microbial, yet within about 100 million years (600 to 500 million years ago), the Animal Kingdom originated, then diversified into nearly all of the major phyla and most of the invertebrate classes and orders subsequently known. Toward the end of the Cretaceous, the dinosaurs disappeared, leaving their econiches to be filled by other reptiles and by amphibians, birds, and mammals. The conclusion is inescapable that something happened to the earth's atmosphere at the onset of each of these two (and other) revolutions.

Never since its birth in the solar system has the earth been a truly solid or stable body, and never has it whirled alone in space. Continents drift, mountains rise and fall, volcanoes erupt, enormous ice sheets come and go, ocean levels change, and the magnetic poles wander continuously, occasionally reversing their polarity (north to become south). Faunal revolutions may have been caused by atmospheric changes originating on earth or by changes induced on earth by visiting bodies (or radiations) from outer space. The Cambrian revolution, for example, may have begun when rising levels of atmospheric oxygen—generated by the first photosynthetic microbes —created a favorable environment for animals and for their rapid speciation. And the disappearance of the dinosaurs, near the end of the Cretaceous, may have been the result of competition from the newly evolved and better adapted mammals.

I favor the theory that extraterrestrial events have been, and will continue to be, responsible for major faunal revolutions. A large meteorite strike on Earth would raise vast clouds of dust that would obscure the sun for years, chilling the atmosphere and precipitating a brief ice age.[11] Radiation from a supernova, even 100 million light-years distant, would penetrate the earth's atmosphere and, through a chain reaction, cause a profound drop in world temperature.[12]

No Two Alike

Thus far I may have stressed the importance of natural selection in the evolutionary process while slighting the importance of variation, or individual differences within the species. Were it not for variation, Nature would have no candidates from which to select the fittest—the best breeders. Variation results from mutations of DNA (or its RNA relative) and from sexual mixing of DNAs, a process known as recombination.

Modern laboratory studies are showing that genes are not the fixed units of heredity they were once thought to be. Early evolutionists believed that a gene is a faithful archivist of hereditary information—that its molecular structure is remarkably stable (although it could be altered by exposing it to intense radiations or to drugs such as mustard gas and peroxides). Earlier notions began to change with the emergence in the 1950s of a new discipline—molecular genetics. Now it is known that genes frequently mutate; they make mistakes; the copies they produce are imperfect. Fortunately, most errors in the replication of DNA are removed by "proofreading" enzymes. Those errors that remain give rise to novel organisms; that is, to living forms that differ from any that have ever lived.

Genetic errors are clearly demonstrated in the very rapid evolution of RNA viruses, or plasmids. Plasmids dwell in a sort of limbo between animate and inanimate matter, parasitizing plants and animals that contain DNA. Mainly because plasmids lack proofreading enzymes, their mutation rate can be as much as a million times that of their hosts.

Many kinds of genetic mistakes can lead to mutations. I offer a short classification, paraphrased, from the writings of Dobzhansky and colleagues.[13]

• A section of a chromosome (a block of genes) may be lost during replication.

• A section may stutter, or copy itself more than once.

• A section may lodge on the wrong daughter chromosome.

• Two chromosomes may fuse, or one may split, or one may be lost entirely.

• Two or more entire sets of chromosomes may move to the offspring, resulting in polyploidy. Common in plants, and exploited by plant breeders, polyploidy is rare in animals.

Moreover, during reproduction a fraction of the hereditary message is commonly transmitted not by units located in the chromosomes but by units located in the surrounding cytoplasm. Although the nature of cytoplasmic inheritance is still puzzling, these units—the mitochondria—can unmistakably influence the offspring.

To think of natural diversity is to think of its deepest root: *chance*, the unpredictable element that turns the course of a bloodline to the right, or to the left, or into a dead-end passage. Genetic mutation and sexual recombinations are expressions of chance. Chance also influences evolution when individuals happen to become founders of a new population on some oceanic island or when they discover an econiche left vacant by the extinction of an erstwhile competitor.

In his mystical book, *Human Destiny*, biologist Lecomte de Noüy wrote that he could accept the importance of chance in our world of "perfect disorder" but could not account for evolution "without the intervention of a parascientific anti-chance." He believed in tele-finalism, or evolution with a direction and a goal.[14]

The Direction of Evolution

Limulus, the horseshoe crab, is the last of an ancient line. It is little changed from ancestors who swarmed in the Triassic seas more than 300 million years ago. Now ageless, suspended in time, it stands apart, neither a proper crustacean (among the crabs and their kin) nor a proper arachnid (among the spiders and their kin). One species of Limulus drags itself along marine bottoms between Maine and Mexico and another along the coast of Asia.

Biologists marvel that Limulus has changed so little, living as it does in the subtidal zone where organic competition is as fierce as anywhere on earth. To be sure, Limulus is secretive, heavily armored, and willing to eat almost any kind of food, but so are certain other animals that scavenge in the subtidal zone.

To reflect on the endurance of Limulus is to wonder, Does evolution move in one direction or does it occasionally reverse itself? Does "progress" describe its motion through time? Because natural selection depends in part on opportunism, reverse evolution or devolution is theoretically possible. A salamander might conceivably revert to a fish *if* its environment were to change over millions of years to one more favorable to fishes than to salamanders, and *if* mutations were to replace at appropriate intervals those fishy genes that the salamander had left far behind, and *if* the renegade salamander were to meet with little resistance from enemies and competitors in its new environment. Surely in the real world the probability of a salamander's reverting to a fish is inconceivably small.

Consider, if you will, the mutation factor alone. Mutations are

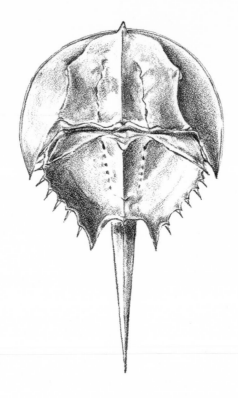

Horseshoe crab

usually harmful. It has been said, facetiously, that the probability of improving a bloodline by causing it to mutate is comparable to that of improving a watch by jabbing it with a nail.[15]

There is, however, a kind of evolution that *seems* to reverse itself. Ancestral penguins could fly; modern ones cannot. But in giving up wings capable of flight, penguins did not reverse in their tracks; they simply advanced on a route that took a hairpin curve. The wings of the modern penguins are not atavistic structures but are strong and dependable swimming organs that were at all stages during their evolution as functional as they are today.

Tapeworms and other parasites have been called animal degenerates. Indeed, the human tapeworm (of which there are several species) is little more than a blind and mouthless sack that hooks itself to the human gut, absorbs food directly through its skin, and sheds enormous numbers of eggs. Yet there are 3,400 known kinds of tapeworms infesting vertebrates as unlike as cold-blooded fishes and warm-blooded mammals. The tapeworm is not, in fact, a degenerate; it has not devolved; it is highly specialized and efficient. What it may have lost in structure it has gained in staying power. Its racial life-expectancy is doubtless no shorter than that of nonparasitic worms.

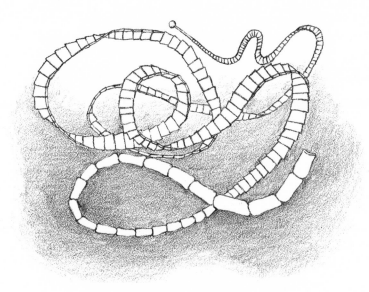

Human tapeworm

As the tapeworm gradually specialized it gave up one ancestral part after another, but so have all multicellular animals. Typical snakes have lost the left lung; what remains is a shrunken vestige. Baleen whales have lost functional teeth. (During fetal development, though, certain tissues in the whale's mouth stir restlessly for a few weeks to produce a set of small teeth which, before birth, are absorbed in the gums.) Similarly, the hind legs of every whale begin to develop in the womb, then disappear. Vestiges of the egg-tooth, the hard part at the tip of the bill or the jaw that enables birds and reptiles to break free of the egg at hatching time, persist in marsupial mammals although 75 million years have passed since marsupial ancestors were obliged to free themselves from shells.

Evolutionists, I think, accept all too casually reports of the occasional whale or dolphin bearing rudimentary hind legs. These monstrosities represent perhaps one in a hundred thousand born. But they are more than monstrosities; they are clues to the origin of a major group of mammals (the Cetacea), and such clues are rare. We can readily imagine how whales would have lost their hind legs. As the protowhales foraged less often in tidal shallows and more often in the open sea, Nature would have favored those individuals having shorter legs—legs that imposed less drag on a body evolving toward the streamline shape.

River porpoise, or susu

We can also imagine how the blind river porpoise, or susu, of India would have lost its sight. This odd little cetacean lives in murky rivers, where it feeds by swimming on one side, swinging its head and echo-locating with ultrasound pulses. Its vestigial eyes are barely visible as small pores in the skin. The susu can distinguish night from day but can't see images. Its ancestors, attracted by riverine fishes, would have moved progressively out of clear marine waters into muddy streams. Eyes would have become useless and, being both energy sinks and sources of microbial infection, would gradually have been selected against.

The loss of functional eyes in the susu is matched by the loss of functional wings in the emu and the cassowaries, flightless Australian birds. Even when selective pressure against a useless structure is weak, the structure tends eventually to disappear, owing, in Julian Huxley's words, to the accumulation of small "mutations that throw the delicate mechanism of adaptation out of gear."[16] No hereditary character persists indefinitely after it has lost survival value, with the unimportant exception of "blurred" characters like nipples on men.

Until recently there lived in Europe a magnificent deerlike animal, the Irish elk. Its subfossil remains are still being unearthed from Ice Age peat deposits. The male bore eighty-five-pound antlers up to *thirteen feet wide* between tips![17] Biologists suppose that the antlers were used for defense against wolves and bears, in courtship battles, and to advertise elk *machismo*.

Two theories offer to explain the extinction of the Irish elk. One holds that body size continued through centuries to increase by straight-line growth, as though Nature had planned an elk but had later mislaid the plan. When both the frame and the enormous antlers of the elk became too energy-costly, the elk went bankrupt. The second, and more plausible, theory is that unknown changes in the European environment put large elk at a comparative disadvantage with smaller, more conservative members of the elk-moose-deer family. Only the smaller ones survived the changes, and these are the species now living.

Skeleton of an Irish elk

I pause in this discussion of evolutionary direction to mention orthogenesis. Nineteenth-century naturalists who were studying fossil
ammonites—coiled molluscs that died out with the dinosaurs—
concluded that evolution has a built-in tendency to move along
straight lines. It has a momentum that carries it along predeter-
mined paths more or less independent of environmental influences.
Evolution, they supposed, has an orthogenetic (literally, "straight descent") tendency.

Well, if orthogenesis *were* a valid concept it would explain why
the antlers of the Irish elk grew larger and larger through successive
generations and why fur seal males came eventually to outweigh

their females 4.5 to 1. But now it is clear that the concept of natural selection has no room for orthogenesis; selection depends on opportunism, while orthogenesis depends on predeterminism. So, no modern evolutionist believes in orthogenesis; the word has taken its place in the history of science along with spiritual ectoplasm, chemical phlogiston, and interstellar ether. I resurrect it only as an example of an evolutionary puzzle that was finally solved.

I don't mean that evolution is wholly random. It does exhibit two tendencies, the first of which is toward speciation. A rational explanation of speciation was first offered to the world on that memorable evening of July 1, 1858, when letters from Darwin and Wallace were read in London to members of the Linnaean Society.[18] The number of species now living—perhaps as many as six million—is probably at its maximum. New species will evolve only at the expense of older ones, for by now all the world's econiches are doubtless taken.

The second tendency is toward large size and complexity of organization. The larger and more complex an organism, the more sophisticated its "computer" equipment, the sharper its awareness of its environment, and the better its ability to solve the problems of that environment. A large and complex organism tends to be more "versatile" and "competent" than a smaller and simpler one. And, as might be expected, complexity in gross anatomy is paralleled by complexity in microstructure. The amount of DNA per body cell varies throughout the five kingdoms from about 0.001 picogram in bacteria to 100 picograms in higher plants and animals.[19] (A picogram is one-billionth of a gram.) The primordial breakthrough from inanimate to animate matter brought a quantum increase in system complexity. Whether complexity is still increasing is unknown, and perhaps unknowable.

The tendency toward large size and complexity is only a tendency, of course, for the Earth is crawling with exceptions. Thousands of lower animals have seen no point in becoming large and complex. But the fossil record stands witness to the fact that the succession of life on Earth *has*, along many bloodlines, been toward the large and the complex. It has led to the evolution of the one large and complex species which alone among animals can write about evolution.

Evolutionary Success

"If the universe was designed to advance toward some state of absolute beauty and goodness, the design was incredibly faulty," wrote Dobzhansky.[20] This thought can be appreciated by humanists and deists alike.

The simplest living organism is as "successful" as the most complex. The whirling molecules that build and maintain the essence of life in microbe and man are identical. Although you and I are larger than the germ, we are no more adequate. And if germs can feel, the average germ doubtless feels as complete as the average man or woman.

Success in human affairs has many meanings: to some the power that comes with money, to others the acclaim that comes with high office or the private awareness that one has fulfilled some task of creativity or stewardship. Success in the animal kingdom can mean surviving unchanged for 50 million years (*vide* the termites), or attaining great size (the 200-ton whale), or claiming 10^{20} relatives (the marine crustaceans known as krill), or occupying a good part of the terrestrial world (the wingless springtail insects). Some evolutionists believe that numerical stability, regardless of absolute numbers, is the best measure of success. They regard a population or species that fluctuates in numbers within a range of, say, 50 percent above and 50 percent below its long-term mean as "well adjusted" or "healthy." (By this measure, the human race rates poorly.)

It is a recurrent idea through history that the living world is an unfinished work, a work in progress, a work reflecting the fumbling advance of Nature toward perfection. "Every being," wrote Buffon, "cherishes its own existence and seeks to expand it, and little by little attains the perfection of its species."[21] Life as a continuous production was termed by Arthur Lovejoy the "Great Chain of Being." But, he warned, "the history of the idea of the Chain of Being—insofar as that idea presupposed . . . a completely rational intelligibility of the world—is the history of a failure."[22] He explained that our cosmos is a cosmos of change and uncertainty. It is one that cannot possibly be reconciled with the model of a reasonable, eternal, and necessary cosmos.

Viewing animal progress from another angle, we might suppose that because the symbolic Tree of Life has grown from its base toward its crown, evolution, too, has moved generally "upward." The phrase, survival of the fittest, coined by Herbert Spencer in 1866, still reinforces popular belief that only the "better" animals survive.[23] But to biologists it is transparently clear that all of Nature's solutions are short term, that the fittest individuals are simply those that bequeath the greatest proportion of their genes to the collective gene-pools of future generations. Fitness can be measured only *post facto.*

The survival, virtually unchanged, of Limulus and other stubborn forms of life is proof that evolution, if progressive at all, is by no means universally so. There exist conservative microbes (fossilized) 3 billion years old that closely resemble living bacteria. And, if a time machine could take us back 70 million years to the place now called Virginia, we might see a recognizable opossum eating a recognizable oyster, for the opossum and the oyster have changed little since the Eocene.

Further proof that evolution is not oriented is the fact that almost no animal organ performs quite the same function for which it was earlier adapted. The flippers of whales and the wings of bats, now used in swimming and flying, stem from the forepaws of terrestrial mammals, and still earlier from the forefins of fishes. Parts of the gill-bearing skeleton of ancient fishes, now transformed and scarcely recognizable, are the bones and cartilages of the Adam's apple you can feel at the base of your throat. And the three small bones in the human ear that carry sound from the eardrum to the auditory nerve have direct antecedents in reptilian jawbones.

Structural diversity in the living world has come about as if an immortal sculptor were forever modeling clay figures, cutting and filling, reshaping bodies, making use of old parts while adding new ones . . . and in time growing displeased with this or that work and dropping it, *holus bolus*, into the recycling bin.

If the word progress *must* be applied to any trend in animal evolution, I believe it might logically be applied to trends that lead toward freedom, in the sense of broad adaptability or versatility. As Simpson puts it: "General progress occurs in changes that are not only adaptive to single environments but also are prospectively more widely useful in other environments."[24] Thus, a progressive animal is one having the potential for continued evolution.

To argue for the reality of progress in the animal world is to defend one's own definition of progress. I suggest that progress is uniquely human and that it began when a hominid first felt "hereness" . . . When that creature looked at dark-skinned fingers and thought, *they move as I want them to* . . . When it thought, *I am me* . . . When it lifted a stone and voiced a word to the lizard that scurried away . . . When it listened to a songbird and forgot for a while that the singer was food . . . When first it could see things that do not exist . . . When first it knew that death must come.

Slowly, progress took on meaning and orientation as men and women came widely to value individual freedom. Freedom has been called by Richard Goodwin "the use and fulfillment of our humanity—its powers and wants—to the outer limits fixed by the material conditions and the material capacities of the time."[25] Freedom is the ideal goal. Sadly, in the meanwhile, far too many of the world's inhabitants live in hollows that hide all goals but the nearest one of security-survival.

Where Is Human Evolution Headed?

Evolution, narrowly defined, is *change*. It is change in the characteristics of populations that share common ancestry and that vary continuously under the influence of internal (or genetic) and external (or environmental) disturbances. To study evolution is to study the very architecture of life itself. To understand the working of inheritance and natural selection, the main evolutionary processes, is to understand why living things vary on a *scala naturae* marked at the lower end by a bacterium and at the upper end by a whale, two forms that differ in body weight as 1 to 10^{25}. It is to understand why Earth can support 300,000 species of beetles, why a female porpoise has eight teats in embryonic life but only two after birth, why a young robin in the nest begs for the worm it has never seen, and why seashells are found in the weathered talus of high mountain peaks.

Natural selection, the process that shaped us until the time around 2 million years ago when we became more human than animal, is now only a feeble factor in our evoluton, for we have become un-natural. Unlike wild animals, we store food with full awareness

Bronze panel from The Seven Days of Creation

of why we do so. Our males rarely fight to copulate with our females but, rather, attract them with words and material goods. We tie the umbilical cord of our newborn young and we bury our dead. And our physicians, swearing the oath of a Greek who lived in the first century before Christ and who could not have known the difference between genetic and cultural evolution, keep alive the unfit as well as the fit.

As we humans become more civilized we seem less able to apply our knowledge of evolution to the improvement of our own Darwinian fitness. In solving the vital problems that we share with other animals—getting food, meeting hard times, defending the self and the family, reproducing, and living in populations—we depend increasingly on cultural guidelines peculiar to our species. We now evolve in a unique environment, the first ever to have been created by rational thought. This is not to say that we cannot solve, within our new environment, the old vital problems, especially the problem of living in populations. The solutions, however, will be more political than biological.

The future evolution of our species is unlikely to depend on the controlled breeding of people for selected characteristics of anatomy and behavior. (Julian Huxley, though, insisted that "eugenics will inevitably become part of the religion of the future, or of whatever complex of sentiments may in the future take the place of organized religion.")[26] Rather, our evolution seems more likely to depend on the exercise of traits that we alone among the animals possess, those of compassion and creativity. By compassion I mean the caring for other humans, for other forms of life, and for Earth itself. By creativity I mean the originality of thought that impels artists, architects, scientists, and other sensitive individuals to cross frontiers into new adventures of the mind. And as long as we survive there will be men and women who will turn again and again to the study of organic evolution, to the study of life flowing through time and space—life coordinated, exuberant, immense and grand, graceful and fine.

Illustration Credits

Exclusive of drawings by Gretchen Daiber and photographs by Victor B. Scheffer.

Darwin, p. 2: J. Pizzeta (A. Hennuyer, Publishers, 1891)
Luminescent squid, p. 22: Carl Chun (Gustav Fischer, 1914)
Termite and trichonymph, p. 25: Turid Hölldobler (Scribners, 1977)
Beaver, p. 33: Hope Sawyer Buyukmihci, 1982
Whistling swans, p. 45: Josef Scaylea, 1982
Tardigrades, p. 46: Ernst Marcus (Gustav Fischer, 1928)
Starry sky, p. 54: Yerkes Observatory, University of Chicago, 1981
Rattlesnake, p. 61: James G. Cooper (U.S. Congress, 1860)
Deep-sea anglerfish, p. 75: C. Tate Regan (Carlsberg Foundation, 1932)
Stomach-brooding frog, p. 78: after a photograph by Michael J. Tyler, 1982
Penguin, p. 80: after a photograph by Frank S. Todd, 1982
Mallee fowl, p. 83: after a photograph by Harold J. Frith, 1962
Quail nest, p. 100: after a photograph by G. Pickwell, courtesy of A. Starker Leopold, 1982
Irish elk, p. 120: W. H. Flower and R. Lydekker (A. and C. Black, 1891)
Bronze panel, p. 125: Jean Johanson

Reference Notes

Introduction

1. John Alcock, *Animal Behavior* (Sunderland, Mass.: Sinauer Associates, 1979), pp. 69–71.
2. Roswitha Wiltschko, Donatus Nohr, and Wolfgang Wiltschko, "Pigeons with a Deficient Sun Compass Use the Magnetic Compass," *Science* 214 (1981), p. 343.
3. Quoted by Loren Eiseley in *Darwin and the Mysterious Mr. X* (New York: E. P. Dutton, 1979), p. 143.
4. George Gaylord Simpson, "Progress in Organic Evolution," *Social Research* 41, no. 1 (1974), p. 51.

The Counted and the Uncounted

1. Robert Hessler, "Oasis Under the Sea—Where Sulphur Is the Staff of Life," *New Scientist* 92, no. 1283 (1981), pp. 741–47. Samuel W. Matthews, "New World of the Ocean," *National Geographic* 160, no. 6 (1981), pp. 792–833.
2. James H. Brown, "The Desert Pupfish," *Scientific American* 225, no. 5 (1971), pp. 104–10.
3. David Lack, *Swifts in a Tower* (London: Chapman and Hall, 1956).
4. Fred Hoyle and Chandra Wickramsinghe, "Where Microbes Boldly Went," *New Scientist* 91, no. 1266 (1981), p. 415.
5. Philip C. Ritterbush, *The Art of Organic Forms* (Washington, D.C.: Smithsonian Institution Press, 1968), p. 61.
6. Paul Tasch, *Paleobiology of the Invertebrates* (New York: John Wiley and Sons, 1973), p. 775.
7. Brent Berlin, Dennis E. Breedlove, and Peter H. Raven, "General Principles of Classification and Nomenclature in Folk Biology," *American Anthropologist* 75, no. 1 (1973), pp. 213–42.
8. Editions of *Systema Naturae* from 1735 to 1770 are described in *Catalogue of the Library of the Zoological Society of London* (London: Taylor

and Francis, 1902), pp. 372–74. Modern nomenclature dates from the tenth edition (1758–59).

9. Lynn Margulis and Karlene V. Schwartz, *Five Kingdoms: An Illustrated Guide to the Phyla of Life on Earth* (San Francisco: W. H. Freeman, 1981).

10. Lynn Margulis, *Symbiosis in Cell Evolution* (San Francisco: W. H. Freeman, 1981), pp. 33, 36.

11. Michael A. Tribe, Andrew J. Morgan, and Peter A. Whittaker, *The Evolution of Eukaryotic Cells* (London: Edward Arnold, 1980). Lynn Margulis, *Symbiosis in Cell Evolution*.

12. Robert H. MacArthur, *Geographical Ecology: Patterns in the Distribution of Species* (New York: Harper and Row, 1972), p. 212.

13. C. Jon Roush, "On Saving Diversity," *Nature Conservancy News* 32 (1982), pp. 4–10.

14. Kenneth Heuer, *City of the Stargazers: The Rise and Fall of Ancient Alexandria* (New York: Scribners, 1972), p. 80.

15. James L. Buckley, "Welcome and Introduction," *Proceedings of the U.S. Strategy Conference on Biological Diversity November 16–18, 1981.* (Washington, D.C.: State Department Publ. 9262, 1982), pp. 9–10.

16. Stuart Kauffman, as reported by Julie Ann Miller in "Evolution: Return of the Embryo," *Science News* 120, no. 1 (1981), p. 12.

17. Theodosius Dobzhansky, *Genetics and the Origin of Species* (New York: Columbia University Press, 1951), p. 3.

18. Gerald L. Wood, *The Guinness Book of Animal Facts and Feats* (Enfield, England: Guinness Superlatives, 1976), endsheet tables.

19. Gerald O. Barney (study director), *The Global 2000 Report to the President: Entering the Twenty-first Century* (Washington, D.C.: Council on Environmental Quality and the Department of State, 1980), v. 1, p. 37 and v. 2, p. 331.

20. John Fowles, "Protect the Word," in *Poems* (New York: Ecco Press, 1973), p. 48.

Problems and Solutions

1. C. H. Curran, "The Human Bot Fly," *Natural History* 44, no. 1 (1939), pp. 45–48.

2. R. B. Frankel, R. P. Blakemore, F. F. Torres de Arraujo, D. M. S. Esquivel, and J. Danon, "Magnetotactic Bacteria at the Geomagnetic Equator," *Science* 212 (1981), pp. 1269–70.

3. Victor B. Scheffer and Ford Wilke, "Relative Growth in the Northern Fur Seal," *Growth* 17, no. 437 (1953), pp. 144–45.

4. Charles Darwin, *On the Origin of Species by Means of Natural Selection* (London: John Murray, 1859), p. 200.

5. Melvin Konner, "She and He," *Science 82*, 3, no. 7 (1982), p. 61.

6. Francis H. Fay, "Ecology and Biology of the Pacific Walrus, *Odobenus rosmarus divergens* Illiger," *U.S. Fish and Wildlife Service, North American Fauna*, no. 74 (1982), p. 39.

7. Carl Chun, *Die Cephalopoden* (Jena: Gustav Fischer, 1910 and 1914), v. 18. Alister Hardy gives a translation in *Great Waters* (London: Collins, 1967), p. 220.

8. B. M. Honigberg, "Protozoa Associated with Termites and Their Role in Digestion," in *Biology of Termites*, ed. Kumar Krishna and Frances W. Weesner (New York: Academic Press, 1970), v. 1, pp. 1–36.

9. Rupert Ormond, "Deceptions on the Coral Reef," *New Scientist* 89, no. 1245 (1981), pp. 730–33.

10. Conrad Limbaugh, "Cleaning Symbiosis," *Scientific American* 205, no. 2 (1961), pp. 42–49.

11. Ibid., p. 41.

12. Ibid., p. 45.

13. John Hurrell Crook, "The Nature and Function of Territorial Aggression," in *Man and Aggression*, ed. M. F. Ashley Montagu (London: Oxford University Press, 1968), pp. 141–78.

14. Paul Shepard, *The Tender Carnivore and the Sacred Game* (New York: Scribners, 1973), p. 123.

15. Willa Cather, *Death Comes for the Archbishop* (New York: Knopf, 1968), p. 50.

Their Daily Bread

1. Karl W. Kenyon, "The Sea Otter in the Eastern Pacific Ocean," *U.S. Fish and Wildlife Service, North American Fauna*, no. 68 (1969). Victor B. Scheffer, *The Amazing Sea Otter* (New York: Scribners, 1981).

2. C. R. Taylor, "The Eland and the Oryx," *Scientific American* 220, no. 1 (1969), pp. 88–95.

3. Daniel P. Costa and Leo C. Ortiz, "Water, Electrolyte and Nitrogen Balance in Fasting Weaned Elephant Seal Pups . . . ," *Physiologist* 23, no. 4 (1980), p. 98.

4. Brian K. McNab, "The Structure of Tropical Bat Faunas," *Ecology* 52, no. 2 (1971), pp. 352–58.

5. Roderick A. Suthers, "Acoustic Orientation by Fish-catching Bats," *J. Experimental Zoology* 158, no. 3 (1965), pp. 319–48.

6. Jared M. Diamond, "Mixed-species Foraging Groups," *Nature* 292 (1981), pp. 408–9.

7. H. L. Bell, "An Association of Two New Guinea Bird Species," *Emu* 67 (1967), pp. 95–98. Martin Moynihan, "The Coincidence of Mimicries and Other Misleading Coincidences," *American Naturalist* 117 (1981), pp. 372–78.

8. Moynihan, "The Coincidence of Mimicries . . . ," p. 375.

9. Ernst Mayr, *Populations, Species, and Evolution* (Cambridge: Harvard University Press, 1970), p. 358.

10. J. R. Norman, *A History of Fishes* (New York: A. A. Wyn, 1948), p. 250.

11. Eugene Willis Gudger, *The Candiru: The Only Vertebrate Parasite of Man* (New York: P. B. Hoeber, 1930).

How They Meet Hard Times

1. John H. Crowe and Alan F. Cooper, Jr., "Cryptobiosis," *Scientific American* 225, no. 6 (1971), pp. 30–36. Boyce Rensberger, "Life in Limbo," *Science 80*, November 1980, pp. 36–43.

2. Garrett Hardin, *Biology: Its Principles and Implications* (San Francisco: W. H. Freeman, 1966), p. 157.

3. Edmund C. Jaeger, "Further Observations on the Hibernation of the Poor-Will," *Condor* 51 (1949), pp. 105–9.

4. R. S. Felger, K. Clifton, and P. J. Regal, "Winter Dormancy in Sea Turtles: Independent Discovery and Exploitation in the Gulf of California by Two Local Cultures," *Science* 191, no. 4224 (1976), pp. 283–85.

5. Lincoln P. Brower, "Monarch Migration," *Natural History* 86, June-July 1977, p. 41.

6. I. C. T. Nisbet, "Measurements with Radar of the Height of Nocturnal Migration over Cape Cod, Massachusetts," *Bird-banding* 34, no. 2 (1963), p. 65.

7. Gerald L. Wood, *The Guinness Book of Animal Facts and Feats* (Enfield, England: Guinness Superlatives, 1976), p. 100. Lawrence W. Swan, "The Ecology of the High Himalayas," *Scientific American* 205, no. 4 (1961), p. 68.

8. T. T. McCabe, "Types of Shorebird Flight," *Auk* 59 (1942), p. 111.

9. Karl W. Kenyon and Dale W. Rice, "Homing of Laysan Albatross," *Condor* 60 (1958), pp. 3–6.

10. Frederick C. Lincoln, "Migration of Birds," *U.S. Fish and Wildlife Service, Circular No. 16*, revised (1979), p. 59.

11. E. G. F. Sauer, "Celestial Navigation by Birds," *Scientific American* 199, no. 2 (1958), p. 43.

12. Ibid., p. 45.

13. Stephen T. Emlen, "The Stellar-orientation System of a Migratory Bird," *Scientific American* 233, no. 2 (1975), pp. 102–11.

14. Ibid., pp. 110–11.

15. William T. Keeton, "The Mystery of Pigeon Homing," *Scientific American* 231, no. 6 (1974), p. 105.

16. Janice G. Mather, "Wheel-running Activity: A New Interpretation," *Mammal Review* 11, no. 1 (1981), pp. 41–51.

17. Janice G. Mather and R. Robin Baker, "Magnetic Sense of Direction in Woodmice for Route-based Navigation," *Nature* 291, no. 5811 (1981), pp. 152–55.

How They Defend Themselves

1. Christopher Gregory Weber, "The Bombardier Beetle Myth Exploded," *Creation/Evolution* 3 (Winter 1981), pp. 4–5.

2. Darwin, *On the Origin of Species*, (London: John Murray, 1859), p. 186.

3. Clifford H. Pope, "Fatal Bite of Captive African Rear-fanged Snake, *Dispholidus*," *Copeia* 1958, no. 4, pp. 280–82.

4. Ernest P. Walker, *Mammals of the World*, 3d ed. (Baltimore: Johns Hopkins Press, 1975), p. 7.

5. Ibid.

6. Bruce W. Halstead, *Dangerous Marine Animals* (Cambridge, Maryland: Cornell Maritime Press, 1959), p. 114.

7. E. J. H. Corner, "The Evolution of Tropical Forests," in *Evolution as a Process*, ed. Julian Huxley, A. C. Hardy, and E. B. Ford (London: George Allen and Unwin, 1954), p. 43.

8. Evelyn Shaw, "Fish in Schools," *Natural History* 84, no. 8 (1975), p. 40.

9. T. J. Pitcher, B. L. Partridge, and C. S. Wardle, "Blind Fish Can School," *Science* 194, no. 4268 (1976), p. 964.

10. Colin Patterson, *Evolution* (London: Routledge and Kegan Paul, 1978), pp. 79–83.

11. Thomas C. Emmel, "Adaptation on the Wing," *Natural History* 84, no. 4 (1975), pp. 82–93.

12. J. V. Z. Brower, "Experimental Studies of Mimicry in Some North American Butterflies," *Evolution* 12 (1958), pp. 32–47.

13. John Alcock, *Animal Behavior: An Evolutionary Approach* (Sunderland, Mass.: Sinauer Associates, 1979), p. 355.

14. Paul W. Sherman, "Nepotism and the Evolution of Alarm Calls," in *Evolution Now: A Century after Darwin*, ed. John Maynard Smith (San Francisco: W. H. Freeman, 1982), pp. 186–203.

15. Ibid., p. 200.

16. Edward O. Wilson, *Sociobiology: The New Synthesis* (Cambridge, Mass.: Belknap Press of Harvard University, 1975).

17. Ibid., p. 3.

18. David Barash, *Whisperings Within: Evolution and the Origin of Human Nature* (New York: Harper and Row, 1979).

How They Breed

1. Alexander Agassiz, "The Islands and Coral Reefs of Fiji," *Bull. Museum Comparative Zoology, Harvard Univ.* 33 (1899), p. 16.

2. M. J. Winterbourn and N. H. Anderson, "The Life History of *Philanisus plebeius* Walker . . . a Caddisfly Whose Eggs Were Found in a Starfish," *Ecological Entomology* 5 (1980), pp. 293–303.

3. Marston Bates, *The Forest and the Sea* (New York: Random House, 1960), p. 95.

4. C. Tate Regan and Ethelwynn Trewavas, "Deep-sea Angler-fishes (Ceratioidea)," *Carlsberg Oceanographic Expedition, 1928–30*, Report no. 2 (1932), pp. 1–113.

5. Ibid., p. 13.

6. "Animal Olympics," BBC's NOVA series, telecast July 28, 1981.

7. Doris M. Cochran, *Living Amphibians of the World* (New York: Doubleday, 1961), p. 106.

8. Michael J. Tyler and David B. Carter, "Oral Birth of the Young of the Gastric Brooding Frog *Rheobatrachus silus*," *Animal Behaviour* 29 (1981), pp. 280–82.

9. Apsley Cherry-Garrard, *The Worst Journey in the World* (London: Constable, 1922), p. 234.

10. Ibid., p. 268.

11. Terry Dunkle, "Chicken Teeth," *Science 80*, v. 1, no. 6 (1980), pp. 94–95.

12. Ibid., p. 94.

13. Darwin, *On the Origin of Species* (London: John Murray, 1859), p. 450.

14. Michael Ruse, *The Darwinian Revolution: Science Red in Tooth and Claw* (Chicago: University of Chicago Press, 1981), p. 95.

15. George Gaylord Simpson and William S. Beck, *Life: An Introduction to Biology*, 2d ed. (New York: Harcourt, Brace and World, 1965), p. 241.

16. Harold James Frith, *The Mallee-fowl: The Bird That Builds an Incubator* (Sydney: Angus and Robertson, 1962). Alexander F. Skutch, "Flight from the Nest," *Animal Kingdom* 77, no. 1 (1974), pp. 10–16.

17. Frith, *The Mallee-fowl*, p. 63 (quoting K. H. Bennett, 1884).

18. Gregory Pincus, "The Development of Fertilized and Artificially Activated Rabbit Eggs," *J. Experimental Zoology* 82, no. 1 (1939), pp. 85–121.

19. Carl L. Hubbs and Laura C. Hubbs, "Apparent Parthenogenesis in Nature, in a Form of Fish of Hybrid Origin," *Science* 76 (1932), pp. 628–30.

20. Roger L. Blackman, "Species, Sex and Parthenogenesis in Aphids," in *The Evolving Biosphere*, ed. P. L. Forey (London: British Museum [Natural History], 1981), p. 77.

21. Ibid., p. 75.

22. David O. Conover and Boyd E. Kynard, "Environmental Sex Deter-

mination: Interaction of Temperature and Genotype in Fish," *Science* 213 (1981), pp. 577–79.

23. David O. Conover, letter to author, 1982.

24. George C. Williams, *Adaptation and Natural Selection* (Princeton, N.J.: Princeton University Press, 1966), p. 154.

25. William S. Spector, ed., *Handbook of Biological Data* (Washington, D.C.: National Academy of Science and National Research Council, 1956), p. 519.

26. Judith H. Myers, "Sex Ratio Adjustment Under Food Stress: Maximization of Quality or Numbers of Offspring?" *American Naturalist* 112, no. 984 (1978), pp. 381–88.

27. Robert L. Trivers and Dan E. Willard, "Natural Selection of Parental Ability to Vary Sex Ratio of Offspring," *Science* 179 (1973), p. 90.

28. John C. Coulson, "The Breeding Biology of the Grey Seal, *Halichoerus grypus* (Fab.) on the Farne Islands, Northumberland," *J. Animal Ecology* 33 (1964), p. 499. Ian Stirling, "Variation in Sex Ratio of Newborn Weddell [and fur] Seals During the Pupping Season," *J. Mammalogy* 52, no. 4, (1971), pp. 842–44.

29. Polley Ann McClure, "Sex-biased Litter Reduction in Food-restricted Wood Rats (*Neotoma floridana*)," *Science* 211 (1981), p. 1059.

30. Ibid.

31. Fridtjof Nansen, quoted by Finn Walvig in "The Gonads and the Formation of the Sexual Cells," in *The Biology of Myxine*, ed. Alf. Brodal and Ragnar Fange (Oslo: Universitetetsforlaget, 1963), p. 574.

32. J. F. D. Frazer, *Amphibians* (New York: Springer-Verlag, 1973), p. 54.

Life in Populations

1. Victor B. Scheffer and Arthur R. Kruckeberg, "The Mima Mounds," *BioScience* 16, no. 11 (1966), pp. 801–2.

2. Thomas E. Kennerly, Jr., "Microenvironmental Conditions of the Pocket Gopher Burrow," *Texas J. Science* 16, no. 4 (1964), p. 438.

3. Richard M. Hansen and Richard S. Miller, "Observations on the Plural Occupancy of Pocket Gopher Burrow Systems," *J. Mammalogy* 40, no. 4, pp. 577–84.

4. Darwin, *On the Origin of Species* (London: John Murray, 1859), pp. 72–73.

5. John B. Calhoun, "Death Squared: The Explosive Growth and Demise of a Mouse Population," *Proceedings, Royal Society of Medicine* 66 (1973), pp. 80–88.

6. Ibid., p. 86.

7. John B. Calhoun, "The Social Use of Space," in *Physiological Mammal-*

ogy, ed. William V. Mayer and Richard G. Van Gelder (New York: Academic Press, 1963), p. 184.

8. David Lack, "Natural Selection and Family Size in the Starling," *Evolution* 2 (1948), pp. 95–110.

9. Ibid., p. 107.

10. F. J. Ebling and David Michael Stoddart, eds., "Population Control by Social Behaviour," *Institute of Biology (London) Symposia*, no. 23 (1978), pp. 283–84.

11. Dennis Chitty, "The Natural Selection of Self-regulatory Behavior in Animal Populations," in *Natural Regulation of Animal Populations*, ed. Ian A. McLaren (New York: Atherton, 1971), p. 136.

12. Charles J. Krebs, "A Review of the Chitty Hypothesis of Population Control," *Canadian J. Zoology* 56, no. 12 (1978), p. 2478.

13. Douglas J. Futuyma, *Evolutionary Biology* (Sunderland, Mass.: Sinauer Associates, 1979), p. 504.

14. Philip J. Darlington, Jr., *Evolution for Naturalists* (New York: Wiley-Interscience, 1980), pp. 100–3.

15. Michael J. Wade, "An Experimental Study of Group Selection," *Evolution* 31 (1977), p. 151.

Tempo and Mode in Evolution

1. George Gaylord Simpson, *Tempo and Mode in Evolution* (New York: Columbia University Press, 1944).

2. J. John Seposki, Jr., "A Factor Analytic Description of the Phanerozoic Marine Fossil Record," *Paleobiology* 7, no. 1 (1981), fig. 5. See also *Nature* 293 (1981), pp. 435–37, for further clarification.

3. Elwood C. Zimmerman, "Possible Evidence of Rapid Evolution in Hawaiian Moths," *Evolution* 14 (1960), pp. 137–38.

4. Stephen Jay Gould and Richard F. Johnston, "Geographic Variation," *Annual Review of Ecology and Systematics* 3 (1972), pp. 457–98.

5. Annie P. Gray, *Mammalian Hybrids: A Check-list with Bibliography*, 2d rev. ed. (Farnham Royal, England: Commonwealth Agricultural Bureaux, 1972).

6. Peter T. Boag and Peter R. Grant, "Intense Natural Selection in a Population of Darwin's Finches (Geospizinae) in the Galápagos," *Science* 214 (1981), pp. 82–85.

7. Darwin, *On the Origin of Species* (London: John Murray, 1859), p. 194.

8. Ibid., pp. 310–11.

9. Peter G. Williamson, "Palaeontological Documentation of Speciation in Cenozoic Molluscs from Turkana Basin," *Nature* 293 (1981), p. 437. See also *Nature* 294 (1981), p. 214, for clarification.

10. David M. Raup, "Taxonomic Diversity During the Phanerozoic," *Science* 177 (1972), pp. 1065–71.

11. J. Smit and G. Klaver, "Sanidine Spherules at the Cretaceous-Tertiary Boundary Indicate a Large Impact Event," *Nature* 292 (1981), pp. 47–49.

12. Dale Russell and Wallace Tucker, "Supernovae and the Extinction of the Dinosaurs," *Nature* 229 (1971), pp. 553–54. George Gaylord Simpson, "Evolutionary Effects of Cosmic Radiation," *Science* 162 (1968), pp. 140–41.

13. Theodosius Dobzhansky, Francisco J. Ayala, G. Ledyard Stebbins, and James W. Valentine, *Evolution* (San Francisco: W. H. Freeman, 1977), pp. 57–58.

14. Pierre Lecomte du Noüy, *Human Destiny* (New York: Longmans, Green, 1947), pp. 41, 51, 247.

15. Earl D. Hanson, *Animal Diversity*, 3d ed. (Englewood Cliffs, N.J.: Prentice-Hall, 1972), p. 30.

16. Julian Huxley, *Evolution: The Modern Synthesis* (New York: Harper, 1942), p. 476.

17. Stephen Jay Gould, "Positive Allometry of Antlers in the 'Irish Elk' *Megaloceros giganteus*," *Nature* 244 (1973), pp. 375–76.

18. Charles Darwin and Alfred Wallace, "On the Tendency of Species to Form Varieties; and on the Perpetuation of Varieties and Species by Natural Means of Selection," *J. Linnaean Society, Zoology* 3 (1858), pp. 45–62.

19. Theodosius Dobzhansky, Francisco J. Ayala, G. Ledyard Stebbins, and James W. Valentine, *Evolution* (San Francisco: W. H. Freeman, 1977), pp. 73–74.

20. Theodosius Dobzhansky, *The Biology of Ultimate Concern* (New York: New American Library, 1967), p. 120.

21. Buffon (Georges Louis Leclerc, Comte de), quoted by Arthur O. Lovejoy in *The Great Chain of Being: A Study of the History of an Idea* (Cambridge: Harvard University Press, 1936), p. 273.

22. Arthur O. Lovejoy, *The Great Chain of Being*, p. 329.

23. Herbert Spencer, *The Principles of Biology* (New York: D. Appleton, 1866–67), v. 1, p. 445.

24. George Gaylord Simpson, "The Concept of Progress in Organic Evolution," *Social Research* 41, no. 1 (1974), p. 51.

25. Richard N. Goodwin, "Reflections. The American Condition," *New Yorker* 69, no. 48 (1974), p. 37.

26. Julian Huxley, *Man in the Modern World* (New York: Mentor, 1948), p. 28.

For Further Reading

Hundreds of books on evolution are catalogued in libraries under author's name, or under Evolution, or under Darwin. Those listed below are a selected sample.

Barash, David. *The Whisperings Within: Evolution and the Origin of Human Nature.* New York: Harper and Row. 1979 (and Penguin Books, 1981). Barash, a University of Washington professor of psychology and zoology, states that "the real subject of this book is human behavior, viewed from the perspective of sociobiology." He suggests the extent to which inherent ("bestial") traits guide our everyday activities. A well-written, widely ranging, and richly anecdotal book.

Brackman, Arnold C. *A Delicate Arrangement: The Strange Case of Charles Darwin and Alfred Russell Wallace.* New York: Times Books. 1980. In this nontechnical book a staff writer for the *New York Times* argues persuasively that Darwin and two friends—geologist Lyell and botanist Hooker—conspired to insure that priority for the theory of natural selection would be credited to Darwin and not to the youthful Wallace.

British Museum (Natural History). *The Evolving Biosphere: Chance, Change, and Challenge.* P. L. Forey, ed. Cambridge University Press. 1981. Articles by twenty-one experts cover the essentials of evolution; certain chapters are rather technical.

British Museum (Natural History). *Origin of Species.* Cambridge University Press. 1981. "This lively and colourful book has been prepared by staff . . . to coincide with the Museum's major centenary exhibition, Origin of Species" (from the book). Beautifully written and illustrated.

Bylinsky, Gene. *Life in Darwin's Universe: Evolution and the Cosmos.* Illustrations by Wayne McLoughlin. Garden City, N.Y.: Doubleday. 1981. After describing how life on Earth did evolve, the author tells us how it might have evolved, had the Tree of Life grown differently. The illustrator shows marsupial "humans," mathematical reptiles, and other imaginary creatures of alternative worlds. These are scarcely less bizarre, however, than some species that now inhabit our planet.

Cherfas, Jeremy (ed.). *Darwin Up to Date*. London: New Science Publications; a New Scientist Guide. 1982. Twenty-two articles culled from the pages of *New Scientist* document the continuing scientific debate on details of Darwinian evolution.

Crick, Francis. *Life Itself: Its Origin and Nature*. New York: Simon and Schuster. 1981. A molecular biologist and Nobel laureate discusses various ways in which life could have originated on the early Earth and, alternatively, ways in which it could have been sent here by beings from another world. Crick explains that the ideal "seed packet" for directed panspermia would have been a frozen mixture of cells similar to Earth's modern bacteria, some of which thrive in oxygen-free, others in oxygen-rich, environments. Simply and understandably written.

Darlington, P. J., Jr. *Evolution for Naturalists: The Simple Principles and the Complex Reality*. New York: Wiley-Interscience. 1980. A college undergraduate text by an emeritus professor at Harvard's Museum of Comparative Zoology.

Darwin, Charles. *On the Origin of Species by Means of Natural Selection, or the Preservation of Favoured Races in the Struggle for Life*. London: John Murray. 1859. Other editions of this classic were published through the sixth in 1872. Harvard University Press published in 1964 a facsimile edition coupled with an introduction by Ernst Mayr, a bibliography, and an index.

Dobzhansky, Theodosius, Francisco J. Ayala, G. Ledyard Stebbins, and James W. Valentine. *Evolution*. San Francisco: W. H. Freeman. 1977. A text for advanced college undergraduates and graduates. The authors believe that their book may be the last one that, in a single volume, can give a reasonably comprehensive account of evolution.

Eiseley, Loren. *Darwin and the Mysterious Mr. X [Edward Blyth]*. New York: E. P. Dutton, 1979. A description of the intellectual climate between 1831 and 1859 when Darwin was formulating the theory of natural selection. Poetic anthropologist Eiseley argues that the basic tenets of the theory were, in fact, published by naturalist Blyth long before the appearance of Origin of Species. Three scientific articles by Blyth (1835, 1836, 1837) are reprinted here.

Futuyma, Douglas J. *Evolutionary Biology*. Sunderland, Mass.: Sinauer Associates. 1979. A good college-level text. The final chapter is on "Social Issues in Human Evolution." Glossary of common evolutionary terms.

Gould, Stephen Jay. *Ever Since Darwin: Reflections in Natural History*. New York: W. W. Norton. 1977. Gould teaches biology, geology, and the history of science at Harvard University. The essays in this book originally appeared as a monthly series, beginning in 1974, in the magazine

Natural History. In the author's words, "they range broadly from planetary and geological to social and political history, but they are united . . . by the common thread of evolutionary theory—Darwin's version" (Prologue). Gould is one of the most brilliant and articulate scholars in the field of evolutionary thought today.

Gould, Stephen Jay. *The Panda's Thumb: More Reflections in Natural History*. New York: W. W. Norton. 1980. More *Natural History* essays, supplemented by hitherto unpublished Gould writings. The "thumb" of the giant panda serves as a launching point for a discussion of animal adaptation.

Handler, Philip (ed.). *Biology and the Future of Man*. New York and London: Oxford University Press. 1970. Eminent scientists present a survey of life-science topics including the origin of life, heredity, evolution, and organic diversity. High-school or college undergraduate reading levels.

Huxley, Julian, and H. B. D. Kettlewell. *Charles Darwin and His World*. London: Thames and Hudson. 1965. A richly illustrated work "designed to bring out the main facts of Darwin's life and the leading principles of his thought" (*London Times*). A pleasureful book.

Margulis, Lynn, and Karlene V. Schwartz. *Five Kingdoms: An Illustrated Guide to the Phyla of Life on Earth*. San Francisco: W. H. Freeman. 1981. A unique catalog of the world's living organisms, this book devotes two or more pages to each of eighty-nine phyla. Each phylum is characterized by word descriptions, illustrations, and sample names of its typical members. For scholarly readers. Glossary.

Mayr, Ernst. *The Growth of Biological Thought: Diversity, Evolution, and Inheritance*. Cambridge: Harvard University Press. 1982. François Jacob's evaluation can hardly be improved upon: "This is a very remarkable book that could have been written only by such a man as Ernst Mayr, who is not merely one of the major evolutionary biologists of this century but also a great philosopher and historian of biology, as well as an exceptional writer. No other book tells in such a lucid and critical way the evolution of ideas that led to modern biology." The book is fully documented, with about 1,300 references and a glossary.

Mayr, Ernst. *Populations, Species, and Evolution*. Cambridge: Harvard University Press. 1970. An abridged and revised edition of his 1963 book, *Animal Species and Evolution*. A college-level text termed by Julian Huxley "the most important study of evolution that has appeared in many years—perhaps since . . . *The Origin of Species*." Glossary.

Mayr, Ernst, and William B. Provine (eds.). *The Evolutionary Synthesis: Perspectives on the Unification of Biology*. Cambridge: Harvard University Press. 1980. Twenty-one evolutionists discuss what is known as "the modern synthesis," or the reconciliation of Darwinian natural selection with genetic (molecular) variation. Mayr contributes a delightful piece, "How I Became a Darwinian."

Moore, Ruth, and the Editors of Life. *Evolution*. New York: Time, Inc. 1962. Although somewhat out of date, this profusely illustrated and easily read book will be useful to general readers.

Newman, William L. *Geologic Time*. Washington, D.C.: U.S. Geological Survey. 1978. A twenty-page booklet that explains how the ages of rocks—up to 4.5 billion years—are estimated from their rates of radioactive decay. A diagram illustrates the major groups of animals, some known only as fossils, characterizing each of the geological eras and periods.

Patterson, Colin. *Evolution*. London: Routledge & Kegan Paul, in association with the British Museum (Natural History). 1978. A zoologist at the Museum summarizes in plain language ideas about how life on Earth began and how it later speciated. Glossary.

Ruse, Michael. *The Darwinian Revolution: Science Red in Tooth and Claw*. Chicago: University of Chicago Press. 1979. A philosopher of science looks at the period between 1830 and 1875 when Darwin was conceiving, giving birth to, and defending the theory of natural selection.

Scientific American. Evolution. San Francisco: W. H. Freeman. 1978. Nine articles previously published in *Scientific American* cover chronologically the origins of life, of cells, of multicellular organisms, of ecological systems, of animal behavior, and of man.

Simpson, George Gaylord. *The Meaning of Evolution: A Study of the History of Life and of Its Significance for Man*. New Haven: Yale University Press. 1967. Simpson, writing at the peak of an illustrious career, summarizes the evolutionary process. His writing is spiced with humor, an uncommon ingredient in scientific literature.

Smith, John Maynard (ed., in association with *Nature*) *Evolution Now: A Century after Darwin*. San Francisco: W. H. Freeman. 1982. This is an anthology of papers from *Nature, Science,* and other scientific journals selected to illustrate certain controversial issues in evolutionary biology. The papers are grouped under six headings: the origin of life, the evolution of the genome, Lamarckian inheritance and the puzzle of immunity, the pattern of nature, evolution—sudden or gradual?, and the evolution of behaviour.

Stebbins, G. Ledyard. *Processes of Organic Evolution*. 3d ed. Englewood Cliffs, N.J.: Prentice-Hall. 1977. A college text. Although Stebbins is a botanist, he understands, and successfully writes about, the evolution of all living things, including humans.

Thackray, John. *The Age of the Earth*. London: Her Majesty's Stationery Office, for the Institute of Geological Sciences. 1980. A popular illustrated booklet telling "how the main divisions of Earth history have been established in terms of geographical and climatic changes and events in the unfolding pageant of life."

Vanderpool, Harold Y. (ed.). *Darwin and Darwinism: Revolutionary Insights Concerning Man, Nature, Religion, and Society*. Lexington, Mass.:

D. C. Heath. 1973. Selected readings that illuminate historical beliefs about the origin of plant and animal species. This anthology features, among other authors, Jehovah (in Genesis), William Cowper, Charles Darwin, T. H. Huxley, Herbert Spencer, and Alfred Lord Tennyson.

Williams, George C. *Adaptation and Natural Selection: A Critique of Some Current Evolutionary Thought.* Princeton, N.J.: Princeton University Press. 1966. Aimed at advanced students in biology, Williams' book speculates on the importance of various factors in evolution. "A beautifully written and excellently reasoned essay in defense of Darwinian selection" (*Science*).

Index

Scientific names of animals featured in the text are in parentheses.